TRANSCENDING TRAUMA

*Post-Traumatic Growth Following Physical,
Sexual, and Emotional Abuse*

GERAL T. BLANCHARD

The
SaferSociety
P R E S S

BRANDON, VERMONT

Library of Congress Cataloging-in-Publication Data
Blanchard, Geral T., author.
 Transcending trauma : post-traumatic growth following physical, sexual, and
emotional abuse / Geral T. Blanchard. — First edition.
    pages cm
 Includes bibliographical references.
 ISBN 978-1-884444-96-8
1. Traumatic incident reduction. 2. Post-traumatic stress disorder—Treatment. 3.
Sexual abuse victims—Counseling of. I. Title.
 RC552.P67B62 2013
 616.85'21--dc23
                              2013031764

Printed in the United States of America
10 9 8 7 6 5 4 3 2 1

P.O. Box 340
Brandon, Vermont 05733
www.safersociety.org
(802) 247-3132

Safer Society Press is a program of the Safer Society Foundation, a 501(c)3
nonprofit dedicated to the prevention and treatment of sexual abuse. For more
information, visit our website at www.safersociety.org

Transcending Trauma: Post-Traumatic Growth Following Physical, Sexual, and Emotional Abuse
$20 plus shipping and handling
Order # WP160

Contents

ONE

From Trauma to Transcendence

Experience is not what happens to you;
it's what you do with what happens to you.

—ALDOUS HUXLEY

You are about to examine trauma from a new and encouraging perspective, one that suggests that post-traumatic growth (PTG), and even thriving, are possible after experiencing tragic events. According to Tedeschi and Calhoun, who coined the term *post-traumatic growth* in 1998, people who experienced PTG reported positive change in five areas: 1) they had a renewed appreciation for life; 2) they found new possibilities for themselves; 3) they felt more personal strength; 4) their relationships improved; and 5) they felt spiritually more satisfied. For these people, trauma was not a derailment of their lives, but rather an event that shook them deeply and put them on a healthier life track.

As we will see in this book, the trajectory of a trauma victim's life is determined not by the traumatic event itself, but by the victim's response to the event. The victim's response, in turn, is strongly affected by the victim's social environment. The influence of the social environment has been seen in studies of American soldiers, where post-traumatic stress disorder (PTSD) is higher among veterans who cannot reconnect with supportive people. The same results were found in a study of Nepalese child soldiers (Korht 2006) and in experiments with lab rats (Plotsky 2008). In each case, the quality of the post-traumatic social environment played a major role in determining whether trauma was the prelude to a breakdown or the initiation of a breakthrough.

This psychological exploration will be imbued with words of hope and encouragement, ideas that I believe will ring true to you as you digest the substantive foundation that post-traumatic growth is built upon. Health-care professionals know that trauma victims need much more than pep talks or cheerleading. They benefit most from solid information, clear guidelines, and real-life examples of people who have blossomed into their best selves following excruciating physical and/or emotional pain. In short, what they need from you is the guidance that will help them make the most out of trying times, a template that can turn adversity into opportunity while steering their lives in the direction of deeper meaning and inner strength. Prepare to sit with some new and invigorating concepts that expand the prevailing PTSD paradigm.

I wrote this book for my fellow health-care professionals, including psychologists, psychotherapists, and social workers, who work in the trauma field, especially those who support victims of sexual abuse. Most of you are probably very familiar with much of the psychiatric literature espousing the "breakage theory" of trauma, describing victims as "shattered vases." Rather than repeatedly referencing existing trauma theory for purposes of comparison, contrast, and argument, I will simply offer a new and consistently positive message of hope that is grounded in research and supported by personal anecdotes and common sense. Again and again, I will assert that specific types of events by themselves do not determine if someone will be harmed by trauma. A victim's response to trauma, including the posture and meaning assigned to the experience, will most likely be the factor that will make or break the individual. What victims believe and how they relate to adversity is every bit as important to recovery as the tragedy itself. Whether a person has been terrorized by sexual abuse, a hostage situation, or a tornado, a resilient response will be required to successfully integrate the experience and grow from it. One challenge for the helping professional is to know all the factors that give rise to growth and fan the sparks of hope into a towering flame. Another challenge is to learn how some types of trauma, sexual abuse as an example, may require additional understanding and a unique language to best tailor an individual treatment plan that will help to assure growth.

There is no one type of definable traumatic event, whether physical, emotional, or sexual, that by itself has greater power than any other to generate a damaging response. What matters most for the creation of lasting injury or a robust rebound is the victim's personal response to what has happened, the way in which the victim relates to the suffering.

In other words, how victims fashion a belief system that makes meaning of their experience directly relates to how they successfully fit it into an ever-changing and expanding life narrative. The way in which individuals are guided to talk about their horrors, and how they flexibly tell their story of those events, sets the stage for either the diagnosis of PTSD or the possibility of a positive transformation. Trauma victims clearly have a vote in the matter. The therapist is charged with focusing the spotlight on every opportunity for empowerment and to support new, wise, and increasingly effective choices. I will discuss some of the methods I have used in my own practice to "focus the spotlight" in chapter 7.

A formal and final diagnosis of PTSD will be presented not as a fixed or final destination for trauma sufferers, but rather as one point on a wide and dynamic continuum ranging from the symptomatic expression of post-traumatic stress all the way to a post-traumatic thriving response. Like others before me (Pearsall 2003; Haidt 2006; Joseph 2011) I will posit that post-traumatic stress is often the starting point for recovery, in fact it is often the impetus for growth. Post-traumatic stress is part of a natural healing process that can serve as a catalytic factor, jump-starting amazing psychological transformations. From that perspective, trauma, and more specifically post-traumatic stress, can be regarded as a necessary and liberating first step for individuals to discover a path of flourishing. While traumas can present in limitless, diverse, and unimaginable forms, there are now documented ways people can respond to pain that eventually help them benefit from the experience; not in every case, but with amazing frequency. The chapters that follow will spell out many of the social, psychological, spiritual, biochemical, and neurological factors that can liberate victims from their past.

As we proceed, I will refer to trauma in many ways: as a crisis, a tragic event, a discomforting wound, a very difficult adversity, and even a near-death experience. All these terms are intended to describe the experiences of pain that naturally and predictably come with being human and being alive. Trauma will not be consigned to just those rare and singularly horrific events that make the evening news, but will encompass what can be just as painful, namely those many smaller yet cumulatively searing experiences that most of us accumulate over a lifetime. As we examine this universally traveled path, you may, perhaps even to your surprise, find the journey to be uplifting and unexpectedly hopeful at times. It should be that way, as the facts about to be presented will support the promise of substantially better trauma outcomes than have been previously considered.

The first step on this path is to define trauma and differentiate it from suffering. Historically, we have regarded trauma as an unexpected, uncontrollable, and frightening injury, whether physical or emotional, severe enough in nature that it can result in disordered conditions at both levels. Additionally, trauma is regarded as an extreme form of stress or fear that can even be life threatening. It momentarily overloads the human system and, in some instances, results in temporary or permanent immobilization, helplessness, hopelessness, and hyperarousal, carrying the potential for significant body dysregulation and mental detachment from reality. In contrast, suffering will be portrayed as the result of our editorial response to pain. It will be described as the negative commentary, the grumbling, complaining, and labeling—in essence all the background noise of our own making that keeps pain alive and can deepen the original wound. Said another way, trauma comes from an external source but is often maintained or exacerbated by an internal process. Suffering can be regarded as the inability to tolerate painful events for any extended period of time. It results from attempts to escape the discomfort of reality, what Buddhists refer to as "what is." A traumatic wound is not limited to something that happened to us in the past; it is primarily the inability to stay connected with our best essence and deeper nature in light of what has happened to us.

To expedite recovery it helps to be surrounded by a community of confident individuals who have effectively squeezed every available lesson, every benefit, from their own brushes with adversity. Usually these folks won't settle for coping or surviving; they want more from life, they want to thrive. There are many such people who aren't satisfied to merely bounce back after adversity. They desire a life lived fully, including the experience of feeling things deeply such as joy, despair, awe, and even pain. Thrivers are people who continue to expand after each and every test, and eventually flourish. For many people, trauma serves to awaken them to this possibility. From these individuals I have heard many inspirational stories and learned a great deal about post-traumatic growth, about being steeled by life's most demanding tests. As more hope-filled individual stories evolve into cultural stories, an entirely new set of social expectations may develop in this country.

Researchers (Breslau and Kessler 2001) have estimated that 75 percent of all people will experience some kind of trauma over their life span. It is a healthy and an adaptive part of living to expect the unexpected. Within a given year, one-fifth of us will experience a potentially traumatic event (Kessler, Sonnega, Bromet, Hughes, and Nelson 1995; Elliot and Briere 1995). The good news is that while it is natural for human beings, and all other creatures, to undergo traumas, it is just as natural for us to shake them off.

Most people have experienced at least one trauma in childhood, usually several. The majority of us, including children, seem to escape the damaging effects of trauma, something psychologists have referred to as resiliency (Karr-Morse and Wiley 2012). The exemplary skills and abilities of resilient children, plus the social support made available to them, along with their inspirational philosophies and spirituality, have contributed much to the field of positive psychology and have illustrated the chapters to come.

The theories and solutions outlined in this book will be woven together by some common threads. The way through suffering comes from surrendering to it, but not by passive acquiescence. The way out is the way through. Recovery comes from befriending pain, experiencing the tension of it, and not trying to resolve it too quickly. An important first step to rebound and then thrive is to refuse to allow associated emotions of grief, fear, and sadness to be labeled as pathological. Being in pain doesn't mean something is wrong with a person; more often than not it means the person is alive, responsive, and normal. By temporarily immersing oneself in the vulnerable emotions of fear, hurt, sadness, and grief one can prevent those feelings from later being transmuted into destructive forces like cynicism, anger, resentment, hate, and vengefulness. Sitting with strong emotions, or as I prefer to call it "surfing emotions," usually does not cause serious problems, whereas avoiding them almost always does. Problems occur when individuals get stuck in their own mental mud, spinning their wheels telling a tragic tale with only one allowable outcome.

Ours is a culture that values the quest for continuous pleasure and, as a result, the immediate elimination of all pain. Many people have settled on the dictum that the pursuit of happiness is what will provide a satisfying life, a life worth living. It is more than an expectation; this pursuit is regarded by many of us as an inviolable legal right, so sacrosanct that it has even been written into the U.S. Constitution. Yet, our country's burgeoning addictions are evidence that this philosophy, when carried to an extreme, is flawed. As a nation we are unwilling to sit with pain or discomfort for very long. Massive amounts of instantaneous, readily accessible sources of pleasure and excitement are used to eradicate life's normal and abnormal discomforts. This process is the very definition of addiction. Antidepressant, anti-anxiety, and mood-stabilizing prescription drugs are readily available to help us tamp down the normal emotional hurt that comes with being alive. At this point in history, Western cultures tend to be reacting in largely fearful ways that are often generated by profitable "neuromarketing" and an irrational shared worldview that is not grounded in scientific facts. This is happening despite the statistics, which reveal that interpersonal violence is plummeting, especially when contrasted with the "good old days" of 10 to 20 years ago when life was far more dangerous. The FBI, the Centers for Disease Control, the American Cancer Society, and the Department of Justice are a few examples of organizations that churn out crime and public health numbers every year that, without expert help in their interpretation, are enough to cause all of us to never leave home without a helmet, a gun, bear spray, and an emergency medical kit. In truth, almost all types of violent crime including homicides, rapes, child physical and sexual abuse, child abductions (the "stranger danger" phenomenon), and online sexual solicitations of children have declined precipitously in the United States and Canada. Teen promiscuity and adolescent risky behaviors are on the decline. Overall, most cancer and cholesterol rates are down too. Despite all this encouraging news, fear of all these presumed epidemics appears to be on the rise (Horwitz and Wakefield 2012; Pinker 2011; Gardner 2009). In confusing times like these, wisdom and clarity sometimes come from the strangest places. I recall the TV cartoon character Bart Simpson once saying to a friend, "People can come up with statistics to prove anything, Kent, 40 percent of all people know that." What we do with trauma can be comparable to what we do with statistics if we operate only from a place of fear.

Living in a time period when the marketing of fear has become very profitable and even trauma industries abound, it is understandable that we have become extremely apprehensive about the awful things that may befall us, albeit of very low probability. Repetitious media exposure to violent events and the corresponding media interpretations of the epidemics that are supposedly engulfing us can shape an exaggerated emotional response. It follows that we would develop symptoms of psychological, physical, and emotional illnesses that match the cultural messages being conveyed by the news/entertainment industry. It is the human inclination to conform individual beliefs to that of the group, to one's tribe or nation. In the process, people tend to erroneously conclude they are suffering from a psychological condition when their community focuses significant attention on frequently described symptoms. External community pressures can easily negate a person's slumbering inner wisdom, the common sense that, if given voice, would contradict cultural exaggerations. Closer examination reveals that most painful emotional events, by themselves, are not intrinsically dangerous to a person's ongoing mental health. Their impact is largely determined by a limited compendium of culturally scripted and programmed responses to widely publicized types of crises, some of which are promulgated by the psychological and psychiatric professions. Clearly, the time to think outside culturally narrow boxes is today.

In my book *Ancient Ways: Indigenous Healing Innovations for the 21st Century* (2011), and in the many magazine articles I've written, I have explored in depth how indigenous cultures and animal friends can provide life skills for people on a journey of healing. In this book, I will offer examples from other societies—often so-called primitive tribes—of how diverse cultures at different historical times have responded in various ways to trauma, some with greater adaptability than others.

Most people are like willow trees, capable of bending down and back, again and again, when faced with a strong wind. Sometimes branches will be broken and permanent scars will remain, but the meaning attached to those powerful shaping events carries the potential to make individuals stronger than before the storm's onslaught. They may never be the same following a trauma. Change is likely. But change in the direction of strength and growth is a strong possibility. In fact, it is a realistic goal for virtually everyone who is languishing in the wake of trauma.

Most everyone can recall inspiring stories about amazing people who surmounted difficult periods in their lives like Nelson Mandela, Anne Frank, Viktor Frankl, Muhammad Ali, Elizabeth Smart, and many more. Their examples are usually remembered because of personal accomplishments unrelated to trauma and by their historical presence in the media. The common theme in their stories is that the troubles they faced in life were actually initiatory experiences, events that elevated them to another more satisfying level of adjustment. The pain of trauma was a necessary ingredient standing between each person and his or her most vital self. The many victims of interpersonal trauma who have come through the doors of my psychotherapy office, whose reputations were not as enormous as the ones I just mentioned, nevertheless have displayed exemplary coffee-shop wisdom, willowy strength, and a rough 'n' tumble grace that brought them home to their elemental best self. They have touched me in ways that were both inspirational and humbling. In the pages to come, I will try to accurately extract the meaning from their struggles and, with the help of current research, craft a message of realistic hopefulness. Tragedy can be taken in any number of directions. This book posits that hope is not a naïve response to trauma. Hope, in tandem with social support and the purposeful search for meaning, is the shorthand prescription for thriving. It is what Native Americans call *good medicine*.

TWO

Resiliency and the Birth of Hope

When crisis exploded in my life, the best in me was born. I found
out what I was really capable of. I discovered who I really am.

—ELIZABETH LESSER in *Broken Open*

Psychological conceptualizations do not evolve until new informa-tion is introduced. Such is the case with stress and trauma. Most of us learned about the Canadian scientist Hans Selye and his pioneering work on stress research while we were in undergraduate school. In the 1950s he introduced the fight and flight responses, which referred to the functioning of our stress mobilization system and was subsumed under his General Adaptation Syndrome. Selye recognized a host of physio-logical responses to stress, particularly in the brain and adrenal glands, and offered medical insights that neurophysiologists are still building on today. Selye made the important distinction between *good stress* and *bad stress*. Until he came on the scene, stress was presumed to have only deleterious effects. Good stress, he posited, was usually entered into by choice, like buying a first home. Bad stress could include the reaction to unexpected trauma. The damaging responses caused by both kinds of stress were said to include alterations of adrenaline production, fluctu-ating cortisone levels, allergies, weakened immune systems, and much more. People can also become addicted to their own stress chemicals where it feels desirable to be flooded by them and their absence feels like something to be avoided (Mate 2003). But overall Selye's conclusion was that complete freedom from stress would not be a desired state; it would be the equivalent of death. He suggested we would all do well to figure out how to cope with all stressors so a long and happy life could ensue.

Redl (1969), a clinician and author, introduced us to the idea of *ego resilience,* which referenced the human capacity to withstand patho-genic pressures, to recover rapidly from a temporary collapse of health, and to bounce back to prior levels of functioning. Redl went further, positing that even without any outside help not only do many people have the ability to return to "normal" after the traumatic weight of adverse circumstances, but a surprising number of people showed supernormal levels of functioning thereafter. At a time when psychiatric literature was exclusively focused on vulnerability and clinical failure in response to trauma, Redl was intrigued by what he observed as an "astounding degree of ego resilience" among victims.

Psychologist Richard Lazarus is believed to have coined the word *coping* in the 1960s. Murphy and Moriarity (1976) later used the language of *coping* to describe normal defensive strategies that even children employ to deal with life pressures. Their studies profiled children who oriented themselves rapidly to difficult situations, who tolerated frustration and anxiety well, and who asked for help as needed. These children were contrasted with vulnerable children who coped poorly in similar situations. The more flexible children were called *good copers*. They showed attitudinal responsiveness in a wide variety of ways, including good insights into interpersonal situations and good feelings about themselves despite undergoing the stressful experiences. Good copers were said to show healthy narcissism. They were inclined to have parents who modeled resilience and created empowering environments, the context of their lives being indicative of the dynamic nature of vulnerability and resiliency that was revealed post-trauma. When setbacks were experienced, good copers were prone to retreat into safety for a while, to take time out to recuperate, to employ self-comforting activities, to play out the traumatic experiences, and they often transformed unpleasant reality by using fantasy.

Other authors stretched our understanding of stress still further, informing us of how we could successfully respond to it. Dr. Herbert Benson, of Harvard Medical School, was one of them. His landmark book, *The Relaxation Response* (1975), was a layman's guide to managing the emotional and physiological responses caused by emotional strain. He developed and taught practical calming skills, emphasizing how individuals can rebound from the deleterious effects of stress. Shortly thereafter Norman Cousins, a biochemistry researcher at the University of California's School of Medicine, penned *Anatomy of an Illness* (1979). In this bestseller, Cousins provided a novel remedy not only for stress but for physical illnesses. It involved the healing power of humor as expressed through the physiology of laughter. He described one of laughter's functions as sending a signal to the body's emergency response system to "turn off," which allowed healing to commence. Cousin's theories were born out of his own hospitalization for a serious arthritic condition during which he elected to use megadoses of vitamin C and large doses of comedic films to recover. As a side note, Cousins was later diagnosed with degenerative heart disease but he went on smiling and laughing for another 36 years.

Swiss psychologist Manfred Bleur (1978) examined the competent responses evidenced in children who lived with adults that were engaged in murderous behavior or incestuous assaults, were grossly neglectful, and/or had psychotic and delusional characteristics—events that would appear to hamper most any child's healthy development. What he learned was that such stressful childhoods did *not* cause inevitable and inexorable outcomes later in life. The children who experienced trauma and went on to develop a sense of purpose and a satisfying life task were inclined to have better outcomes. He concluded that pain and suffering often resulted in a "steeling effect" for many children, rendering them capable of mastering life with all its impediments.

In essence, all of the aforementioned theorists were addressing resiliency, the bouncing back phenomenon, and life satisfaction after encountering painful stumbling blocks. Each person was positing that how individuals respond to stress is vitally important, but stress itself is not inherently the enemy. For the most part, they contended there is a subtle but important difference between reacting and responding. A *reaction* to external stress or trauma tends to be automatic and reflexive, occurring without much thought. A *response*, however, suggests conscious observation and therapeutic choices that can guide an inner healing process. Resilient people don't wait for others to come to their rescue. They have or develop a strong inner locus of control and, quite likely, a strong belief system that is quickly activated after experiencing any significant amount of stress. They choose their thoughts and future orientation quickly, even when under pressure.

Even before the language of resiliency was introduced, the construct was observed and described as *invulnerability* (Anthony and Cohler

1987). Researchers argued that certain types of stressful experiences, when addressed amid a strong support system, could inoculate the recipient against later difficult events. Vulnerability and invulnerability were placed on a continuum, each of us having weaknesses and strengths that could infect us with, or immunize us from, emotional pain. This thinking led psychologists beyond the *victimization hypothesis* that was drawn from studies of extreme situations, such as combat and concentration camps, and returned the focus of their studies to everyday threats faced by most all people.

Resiliency gained traction with the 1988 publication of *Resilience* by Frederick Flach. A psychiatrist by training, Flach's respect for his patients likely had something to do with their good recoveries, in addition to their innate or developed personal attributes. He referred to them as some of the "healthiest people I know" (xiii). Flach wrote, "Many of them had appropriately collapsed in the face of significant stress and change. What on the surface may have looked like a failure to cope was, in fact, evidence of resilience" (ibid.). Flach theorized that the strengths people use to master cycles of stressful disruption and reintegration make up resilience. And resilience, Flach later contended, can be learned. He noted a series of attributes common among resilient patients. In condensed form they include the following:

- A strong, supple sense of self-esteem
- Independence of thought and action, without fear of relying on others, or the reluctance to do so
- The ability to give and take in one's interactions with others, and a well-established network of personal friends, including one or more who serve as confidants
- A high level of personal discipline and a sense of responsibility
- Recognition and development of one's special gifts and talents
- Open-mindedness and receptivity to new ideas
- A willingness to dream
- A wide range of interests
- A keen sense of humor
- Insights into one's own feelings and those of others, and the ability to communicate them in an appropriate manner

- A high tolerance of distress
- Focus, a commitment to life, and a philosophical framework within which personal experiences can be interpreted with meaning and hope, even at life's seemingly most hopeless moments

(ADAPTED FROM *Resilience*, 113–14)

Wolin and Wolin (1993) authored a very helpful book titled *The Resilient Self: How Survivors of Troubled Families Rise Above Adversity*. From their individual perspectives as a psychiatrist and a psychologist, the couple described patients who universally showed resilience, demonstrating abilities to turn adversity into advantage. They observed how patients commonly emerged from adversity with added strength. Their clients picked their way through "psychological mine fields" with a tolerance for frustration, a zest for seemingly impossible puzzles, careful planning, and with deliberate actions. Instead of resorting to useless blaming, resilient individuals—children included—were solution oriented, using their time to search for answers to their predicaments. Of significance to understanding resilience, the Wolins noted how children from difficult families had a healthy habit of *straying*. By straying they were referring to the habit of rising to the challenge of their unhappy homes by making themselves scarce. When tensions rose on the home front, resilient children understood when to disengage; they were endlessly inventive in finding places to go to. Early on they figured out how to use distance to mitigate the toxicity of unhealthy parents or family members. Some of these children trusted their intuition that, "Maybe all this craziness isn't all about me; maybe it's about Mom and Dad." Unlike so many of us who are inclined to put our parents on a pedestal, resilient children were described as seeing their pathological parents more as suspects than sages. They instinctively understood that their family was not what it was supposed to be and therefore they refused to personalize much of the turmoil and mistreatment that occurred at home.

Resilient people, Al Siebert (2005) wrote, are "discovered" personalities. They are curious people who quickly learn from their experiences. Painful events are learning opportunities for them. They get better and better at handling difficult situations because of what they have learned from adversity along the way. Siebert used a term common to cognitive and positive psychologists, *explanatory style,* to reference the way people assign meaning to the events of our lives. A highly dynamic explanatory style has, again and again, been linked to thriving. Resilient folks seem to be able to understand exploitive behavior in others, in part because of their disinclination to categorize people. Unlike many of us trained in psychology, resilient individuals did not suffer from "hardening of the categories." Instead of thinking of others as nouns or things (e.g., borderlines, perverts, psychopaths, idiots, etc.) they are inclined to see the complexity of the human personality more clearly and, as a result, have extra clarity when it comes to drawing conclusions regarding the attribution of responsibility, thereby depersonalizing a perpetrator's motives and relinquishing unnecessary guilt. Additionally, resilient individuals don't wait around for other people to rescue them; they don't look for a white knight but are inclined to search inside themselves for solutions.

In the 1990s, Jon Kabat-Zinn began researching, writing, and teaching us about the role of "mindfulness" in managing stress and chronic pain. Promoting a Buddhist theory of acceptance for whatever is present in our emotional lives, he assured us that staging a war against any disease or stressful life situation would likely be counterproductive. Similarly, Dr. Daniel Segel has been very influential over the last decade promoting his *interpersonal neurobiology model.* His model relies on developing personal skills to harness the social circuitry of the brain for health benefits, which is particularly important following trauma. By using the ancient technique of mindfulness, adults and children could be taught how to do body-scans to resolve body dysphoria resulting from the stress of sexual abuse trauma. They used this self-soothing technique to regain mastery over their bodies and minds, discovering an internal way to restore a calm and steady state. "Tuning into the self also promotes a foundation for resilience and flexibility" (Segel 2010, 86).

Resiliency is now being discussed in popular magazines. In an article entitled "How to Bounce Back Better" (*Health* 2012, 97), a University of Texas professor, Mary Steinhardt, advised readers, "We need stress to grow. It's like working out: You're not going to get stronger unless you stress the muscle." The article also referenced a study from the University of Buffalo that noted how people with chronic back pain were able to get around better if they had experienced serious adversities (illness, divorce, or surviving a natural disaster), whereas individuals who had breezed through life without any serious problems became more impaired. Additional experts on resiliency emphasized the importance of avoiding a negative script while recognizing the power each of us has to change our attitude and actions when bad times arrive. Trauma should not be allowed to interrupt learning. In fact, trauma may call into question some of our habituated and ineffective ways of living. To get unstuck following a crisis, Karen Reivich of the Penn Resiliency Project suggested asking ourselves four key questions (paraphrased) that tap into our "inner MacGyver":

1. What other things [besides my first conclusions] might have contributed to this problem?
2. If I shared this issue with my friends, what would they see as having caused it?
3. What parts of the problem can I directly control, influence, or leverage?
4. What solutions have I not tried yet?

As you might note, the questions could be particularly useful for a sexual abuse survivor who is obsessing on the same questions over and over again, like "Why me?" or "What did I do to provoke this?" They may also help reduce the pervasive feeling of helplessness that frequently arises after a sexual assault. Of all the recommendations made, the real key to recovery was the importance of social connections, and developing and maintaining supportive ties.

Group Resiliency: The Mind of a Nation

Much has been written about resilient individuals, but there are also astonishing examples of how groups of individuals—families, communities, cultures, and nations—have displayed the capacity to recover from harmful situations (Zolli 2012). This is not intended to ignore the ongoing struggles of oppressed groups, like the Native Americans (who still suffer from a multi-generational spiritual malaise following many years of governmental oppression and boarding school abuses), yet, from the examples of groups that are overcoming systematic persecution, hope can be extracted from their expurgation of past terrors.

In a 2012 visit to Rwanda, where nearly one million people were systematically exterminated via shootings and beheadings, often after being raped, I observed a nation that appears to be making amazing strides toward recovery, fashioning hope atop their bloodstained soil. As with the Jewish Holocaust there is the desire to "never forget." But even though the Rwandan national quest for redemption is comprised of many less than perfect attempts at forgiveness, they maintain a persistent desire to move forward without resorting to a frenzy of vengeance and recycled violence. The restorative justice practice of *gacaca* is a council of elders that convenes court in fields of grass. There two visible paths diverge symbolizing the pivotal choice every killer must face, whether to listen to the pain he inflicted on the victims and their families, admit his crimes, and express honest remorse, or to be uncooperative and return to prison to complete his term. If forgiveness is granted, the court will likely sentence him to work in the village where his crimes were committed, usually for several years, performing manual penance in exchange for redemption. By forgiveness the acts of brutality are not overlooked and certainly not forgotten. Rather, a decision is made to no longer hold the perpetrator responsible for how the victim is going to feel from the day of *gacaca* forward. The victim takes charge of his/her emotional health from that point on. There is the recognition that this is not ideal restorative justice, but with such massive levels of criminality, some process had to be developed based on principles of decency that allowed the previously warring tribes to live together again, not as Hutus and Tutsis, but as Rwandans. Some cynics believe *gacaca* may have been motivated by economic concerns, to empty the bloated prisons (Temple-Raston 2005). Nevertheless, this nation is undergoing a novel experience in healing and justice—and they are doing it with amazing grace. They are carrying their pain with a national dignity that is intended to deliver a message to the rest of the world: we remain committed to learning and growing from this enormous human tragedy. They intend to make something good out of their historical reign of terror.

The Stages of Recovery

There are five stages of trauma adjustment that most people go through (Joseph 2011). The first stage has its onset immediately after the trauma, what some call *outcry,* and it is a period of stunned confusion. The shock is often profound and people in this stage may appear as though they are bewildered or in a daze. The second stage is marked by *numbness and denial* and sometimes can occur before the outcry. In this phase, victims may show signs of dissociation or depersonalization, perhaps reporting how they see themselves from a distance, as if they are in a play or perhaps a dream. Stage three is characterized by *intrusive re-experiencing.* In a paradoxical way, it has been demonstrated that the more people attempt to *aggressively* suppress unpleasant thoughts of their trauma, the more frequently the images and memories re-appear. Sometimes this is referred to as the *rebound effect.* In stage four, the *working through* phase, a person may no longer resist thinking about the trauma as much and tend to titrate memories, showing a willingness to remember painful events even if just for a brief time. In the fifth stage, the *completion* phase, denial and flashbacks decrease, and the painful experiences are integrated into the victim's overall life narrative.

Similarly, Warschaw and Barlow (1995) have theorized there are three stages of resiliency:

The first stage, *holding on,* is about the tendency to cling to the past even when it isn't serving you well. This very human tendency, at least on the surface, seems to belie common sense. For instance why do some people stay in harmful relationships that prevent their growth? Usually the answer is that there is a misleading feeling of safety that comes from sticking with the familiar. The surviving grace is a simultaneous tendency to hold on to their deepest beliefs and values that have proven worthwhile in times past. The resultant faith and hope eventually provide a springboard for growth. After people are empowered by solid ideas, they are just a step away from being further empowered by their own rewarding actions.

In the second stage of resiliency, victims are compelled to *let go.* The lessons garnered from their painful experiences establish a footing while the extraneous details of their story fall away. They begin to speak about their life differently, more optimistically, especially after noting demonstrations of their own courage and success. This is the most difficult stage because to become convinced that things can and do change for the better requires a fair amount of supporting evidence. Letting go can create a temporary void, an identity that seems incomplete without the old storyline, but the realistic hope that things may very well change for the better can create excitement over where this journey may take them. This is often enough to sustain positive momentum, especially when the incomplete story of their journey is given a voice in a supportive social network.

Finally, in the third stage the trauma victims enter a *moving on* period. With the empty space in their personal narrative, it becomes a necessity to embark on a new path. This path is once again grounded in and guided by their best values that I call their North Star work. They take a calculated leap into unfamiliar territory. Succeeding in the jump, confidence is born and retreat becomes unlikely. At this level of adjustment victims of trauma are not inclined to look for someone to rescue them; they take charge of their own circumstances by tapping skills learned along the way. Neat and tidy as these steps may seem, many stimulating elements (explored later in this book) must be present at each stage for growth and success to unfold.

Emotional intelligence (Goleman 1995) includes the ability to identify, assess, and manage emotions. It entails self-awareness, motivation, self-regulation, empathy, and adeptness in relationships. When these talents are translated into a resilient lifestyle, they reveal *emotional competence.* Following trauma, a heightened level of emotional intelligence is necessary to recognize the emotional vampires that victims are regularly in contact with and disentangle their lives from such toxic personalities. Emotionally intelligent people demonstrate an expanding personal flexibility in social relations entailing skills of mindfulness that are reflected in their ability to handle difficult people. Interpersonal trauma often increases emotional sensitivity—sometimes too much—but it can be developed into a useful gift. As Muller (1993, xiv), in his aptly titled book *Legacy of the Heart: The Spiritual Advantages of a Painful Childhood,* wrote, "Childhood pain encourages us to watch things more closely, to listen more carefully, to attend to the subtle imbalances that arise within and around us. We develop an exquisite ability to feel the feelings of others, and to become exceptionally mindful of every conflict, every flicker of hope, or despair, every piece of information that may hold some teaching for us."

Resilient trauma thrivers use their emotional intelligence to manage change and chaos. They have what Siebert (2005) calls *counterbalanced qualities.* Their emotional complexity enables them to display slightly contravening personality traits that often serve them well depending on the ever-changing situations they find themselves in. Perhaps they naturally became chameleons to survive as children at home, but now as adults they have fashioned a similar social skill that allows them to be masterfully adept at adjusting to the ebb and flow of each and every interpersonal situation. Examples of these qualities include being:

- Serious and playful
- Industrious and leisurely
- Altruistic and selectively selfish
- Self-critical and self-appreciative
- Cautious and appropriately trusting
- Spontaneous and thoughtful
- Outgoing and able to enjoy solitary time
- Talkative and reflective
- Sensitive and strong

There are certain beliefs that contribute to a resilient mindset. Often these beliefs geminate in young people living in a family environment of help, optimism, and meaning. This environment teaches and models a life posture characterized by many of the following tenets:

- Life problems become worse when we expect our existence to be free of thorns and easier when they are explained as natural initiatory experiences.
- Being proactive is more gratifying than being reactive.
- Being connected to supportive people while being capable of acting independently is valued.
- Challenges are welcomed; they are described as opportunities that test individuals and encourage growth, as well as develop mastery and a sense of empowerment. A series of graduated challenges, mastered through step-by-step planning, gives rise to later life resilience.
- Personal goals are important. Early on they are discussed, explored, and fashioned.
- Resilient people find their calling—the meaning and purpose of their life—which eventually becomes an important part of healing.
- Formulate ethical principles. Knowing what one stands for will be a guide for the good times as well as for the difficult times.
- Resilient people are taught how to see the big picture. They do not get lost or immobilized in the minutiae of their immediate situation. They can see where they are at and where they are going.
- Life is uncertain and does bring suffering. Developing a wide range of tools and a support network can help to surmount periodic challenges.
- Recognize that risks can be as wise as they can be foolish, but when thoughtfully explored, they can be regarded as holding potential for a better life.
- Believing in fate and destiny are regarded as signs of surrender, a passive stance that doesn't net many satisfying results.
- Unpleasant emotions are not to be feared. Riding them out until they dissipate becomes a useful strategy. Early on, resilient people are willing to identify and process their pain.
- A person's greatest enemy is usually himself and that person can be monitored and controlled.

- Fighting a problem isn't always wise. Knowing when to surrender is important so one can detach and move on.
- Have a firm grasp on reality but periodically escape into fantasy. Creative thinking and the use of imagination can open new doors for growth.
- Resist many of the damaging effects of stress by remembering to laugh.
- A resilient mindset can see the positive side of misfortunes. After a tragedy, *counterfactual thinkers* can easily imagine how much worse things could have been and often see potential disasters as lucky developments.
- Recognize that forgiveness can be helpful, especially if it isn't rushed before an imbalance has been corrected or an effort to right an injustice has been attempted. Otherwise sanitizing thoughts and feelings can sap vital healing energy.
- Many indigenous cultures teach their young that traumas, illnesses, and natural disasters are living entities. As such they are advised to talk to them; in other words, engage them in a relationship.

The Biology of Resiliency and Joy

Stress and trauma can create wear and tear on the human body. Don't overlook the fact that the brain is part of the body, it is a *mindbody*. For most every bodily insult that trauma can inflict, there is a corresponding treatment strategy that can be fashioned for healing. By knowing how to fortify the body in advance of traumas, as well as after they have occurred, a person's resiliency quotient can be expanded. This can be achieved through a thoughtful exercise campaign and a wise diet that replenishes the nutrients stress drains from the body.

Emotional trauma can impact physical health in many ways by creating an over-reactive stress response system. Professional literature has documented how many victims have responded to child abuse, domestic abuse, chronic terror, and other forms of psychological battering, with a withering away of their vitality, energy reserves, and overall health.

Immune systems can be impaired by stress and a host of ailments have been tied to trauma in one way or another including chronic fatigue, fibromyalgia, inflammation, elevated cholesterol, hypothyroidism, irritable bowel syndrome, adrenal gland fatigue, anxiety disorders, depression, high blood pressure, premature aging, insomnia, allergies, lupus, weakened immune systems, and underactive stress response systems. Our experiences translate to our biology; mind does alter matter. The stress of trauma, even a trauma that is not remembered by the brain, has chemical and neurological reverberations.

Trauma can take a tremendous toll on the brain, even prenatally, and a mother's stress can harm her baby more than herself (Karr-Morse and Wiley 2012). Wear and tear of stress on a pregnant woman clearly has a deleterious impact on the unborn child's developing brain. An accumulation of emotional blows on the baby's nervous system can cause brain damage. We now know that whether an infant is still in the womb or recently born, high stress can damage the brain in the following ways:

- The amygdala, our brain's fear center, is the first area of the brain to develop and is therefore the first area to be impacted by stress. Neurons in the brain are prone to kindling and can be excited easily even with little outside stimulation. Very early on the amygdala can develop a hair-trigger switch with a propensity to switch to "on" when experiencing even the slightest fear, and later have a hard time resetting itself.
- High stress can cause a loss of brain cells and shrinkage in the hippocampus region, which is responsible for storing memories.
- Stress over-activates the brain's limbic system (including the amygdala, the basal ganglia, and the hippocampus), which can set a person's mood in a dysphoric state.
- Damaging alterations in brain chemicals (like the stimulation of *catecholamines*) can occur, causing potentially unpleasant or even harmful alterations in the production of neurotransmitters (e.g., epinephrine and norepinephrine) and hormones (e.g., cortisol). Alterations in key brain chemicals can alter

mood, lower energy, advance the aging process, and sap joy from people's lives.

- The same brain regions that interpret and detect physical pain are also activated during the experience of emotional rejection and social ostracism; physical pain and emotional pain being experienced in similar ways (Eisenberger 2003).

There is good news! Never before have we had such a good understanding of how the human brain and the rest of the body can be replenished after trauma. In response to all the assaults on the human body, there are an array of remedies that can calm and balance the stress response system, counteract the damage to the brain and body, and according to some research even reverse the aging response (Brown and Gerberg 2004). It is possible to get a head start on trauma by preventively nurturing our bodies throughout the life span, but even after a trauma has occurred, there is much that still can be done to help the body recover and grow to be resilient.

Yoga, which means *union,* is a practice that teaches mental discipline along with physical stretching and exercise. It helps the mind every bit as much as the rest of the body. Study after study now strongly supports the long-held intuitive hunch that one of the best ways known to rebound from stress and to re-inhabit your body is to follow a regular yoga regimen. Not only that, but yoga practice can also help restore the body's immune system and reduce the inflammation that is at the core of so many diseases. Yoga has been shown to slow the biological clock—the aging process—thereby increasing longevity. It lowers cholesterol, reduces blood pressure, increases libido, eradicates depression and anxiety, enhances sleep, improves physical stamina, and increases overall life satisfaction (Broad 2012).

Very recently a specific yoga practice has been developed for trauma survivors and thrivers; it is called *trauma-sensitive yoga* (Emerson and Hopper 2011). It rests on four main foundational themes: 1) It is important to strengthen the ability to be in and experience the present moment (not being primarily oriented toward the historical trauma); 2) it is important to make mindful choices (to be less reactive and more empowered by reason); 3) it is important to take effective action (*demonstrable efficaciousness,* or the development of an inner locus of control); and 4) it is important to create inner and outer rhythms (being in sync with self, others, and the world). Based on the teachings of Besel van der Kolk who believes trauma is a disease of "not being able to be present," this form of yoga helps individuals set aside the irrelevant demands of the past that previously plotted an unhealthy life path. Trauma-sensitive yoga can also release traumatic memories that are stored and "remembered" in the body. And it also helps reduce the sensation of always being on guard by momentarily shutting off the brain's alarm system so that a person can have a recess from being continuously hypervigilent.

All forms of yoga inherently teach trauma victims a variety of ways to recruit their bodies as allies and decode previously overlooked sensate communications. Yoga helps them reconnect with and re-inhabit their bodies. They learn how to become comfortable with unpleasant sensations, to temporarily experience them and, through increased awareness (rather than avoidance), witness discomfort diminishing. The best instructors are inclined to use invitational language, not mechanical instructions, as their students learn to *explore* and *observe* their bodies, and to *notice* specific sensations. Yoga practitioners also *discover* parts of the body that are usually pain free, something that all too frequently goes unnoticed among trauma victims.

My personal yoga practice, Hatha, a branch of Tantra, dates back to about 1400 AD. With that long history I feel satisfied in labeling it as a "time-tested best-practice" approach to mind and body healing. In my classes the instructor uses a term that resonates well with me: *interiorization.* I understand it to mean mindfully looking inward and understanding the ways of our bodies and emotions. While it is our cultural habit to look for external causes and solutions for most everything, addictions and addiction recovery being classic examples, ancient wisdom traditions encourage us to be emotional spelunkers. As explorers we crawl around in the dark recesses of our minds to understand our inner workings, the fears that drive as well as awaken us to our hidden strengths. Meister Eckhart long ago said, "We know so many things but we don't know ourselves. Go into your own ground and learn to know yourself there." That is an apt description of interiorization.

Physical exercise, especially aerobic workouts, are not only an effective way to prevent illness, they are a marvelous way to mitigate the damaging effects of stress. By swimming, biking, running, kayaking, or brisk walking we can activate our body's own drugstore to prepare and release natural opioids. Enkephalins and endorphins are painkillers and mood enhancers, nature's way of taking care of its children without the harmful side effects of many commonly prescribed drugs. The human body is the best pharmacy ever, always knowing and manufacturing the natural healing concoction that is needed, in exactly the right amount, with nary an unpleasant side effect or exorbitant bill to follow.

The Chemistry of Joy (Emmons 2006) offers a variety of world wisdom, old and new, that can help individuals develop resiliency. Each person encounters unique life circumstances and may have a unique temperament and body type that responds to trauma in its own way. Consequently, we are advised to consider a number of healing disciplines and wisdom traditions to foster a resilient response to psychological stressors. Among them are Buddhist-defined emotional types, Ayurvedic body types, and nature flow systems. Nueorpsychiatrist Eric Braverman, in his book *The Edge Effect* (2005), suggested each of us has a unique brain neurotransmitter nature (type) that, when in an imbalanced state, can lead to many common affective and information processing disorders. Most of these maladies can be safely and successfully treated with natural foods and supplements. He believes proper nutrition can reduce anxiety and depression, improve memory, sharpen alertness, and improve mental focus. Braverman prudently advises health-care professionals to test first for neurotransmitter deficiencies, especially serotonin, acetylcholine, GABA, and dopamine, before adding more chemicals to the patient's brain soup. Drawing from a plethora of information summarized by Emmons, Braverman, as well as Cass and Barnes (2008), many nutritional supplements can buttress good meals to create an optimum diet for mental health, thereby enhancing a person's overall physical and emotional resiliency.

If you are considering any use of vitamins, herbs, amino acids, minerals, and hormone supplements it is best to consult with a knowledgeable physician or naturopath before embarking on any personal regimen. As with pharmaceutical antidepressants, many people discontinue using supplements too early when immediate results are not immediately detected or if discouraging side effects arise. To optimize the benefits of legitimate supplement treatments, be sure to research a) whether they should be taken with food; b) what time of day they should be ingested; c) the proper dosing amount for your weight; and d) possible interactions with prescription drugs. For instance, bipolar disorder is a serious and potentially dangerous form of depression, and while very large amounts of fish oil have been useful in its treatment, it may take months before its effects are noted, consequently professional monitoring of its use (alone or in conjunction with other medicines and supplements) is recommended.

Trauma is about extreme stress and stress wears the body down in many ways. Frequently, trauma victims develop eating disorders and, as a result, suffer from inadequate diets. Deficient in nutrients necessary to fuel the brain and heal the body, they may age rapidly. But it doesn't have to be this way. One of the most encouraging news bulletins coming out of the fields of nutrition and holistic medicine has to do with *adaptogens.* Their use in promoting resiliency has been widely researched in Western Europe, Japan, China, India, and Russia. Adaptogens are a special class of herbs that a) increase the body's resistance to a broad range of health threats; b) normalize the body and mind after pathological onslaughts like trauma have occurred; and c) carry no serious threat of physiological disturbance or side effects (Brown 2004). Even though adaptogens have been used for centuries, surprisingly little is known about them in the United States. Their safety and efficacy suggest they should be considered as an adjunct to any medical or counseling program designed to treat the sequelae of trauma. While we now know that stress hormones keep our body running on overtime and can cause it to surrender to many ailments, adaptogens have the remarkable ability to help individuals rebound from stress in a variety of ways and slow down degenerative processes. These nutrients have anti-aging qualities that arise from a) bolstering cellular defenses; b) preventing free radical damage to cell membranes; c) balancing and restoring the stress response system; d) improving metabolic functions that protect against oxidative damage and counteract fat storage;

and e) reducing inflammation, which is at the core of many diseases (Abadoff 2004; Brown 2004).

Adaptogens have long been widely documented to decrease depression (Krasik 1970; Brichenko, Krupiyanova, and Skorokhova, 1986) and improve sleep quality (Brown 2004), but they also have been shown to help patients recover from brain injury due to head trauma (Spasov 2000); they strengthen immune system functioning by increasing the production of natural killer cells and T cells that fight bacteria, viruses, and cancer; and guard against the release of excessive amounts of stress hormones including cortisol, epinephrine, and norepinephrine (Brown 2004). Fatigue is diminished by certain adaptogens (Saratikov and Krasnov 1987). Diminished sexual interest has been reversed with the help of these herbal nutrients. Brown writes (2004, 170), "As far as we know, *rhodiola rosea* [an adaptogen] is the only treatment that can enhance sexual desire, arousal, and capacity for orgasm in women, as well as heighten sex drive in men—all without any serious side effects." What a nice alternative they provide over pharmaceutical treatments for depression, which notoriously have side effects that can curb sexual desire, cause lubrication problems, result in erectile dysfunction, and inhibit orgasm.

Adaptogens are readily available in the United States and in addition to being well tolerated, they are surprisingly inexpensive. They are often sold in blends that include the following ingredients, a few of which you may have heard about:

- Panax ginseng
- Eletherococcus
- Rhodiola rosea
- Schizandra
- Ashwagandha
- Reishi mushroom
- Astragalus root

⌒

Social supports, thoughtful parenting, individual psychotherapy, exercise, supplementation, and nutrition are all powerful components in preventing potential debilitating effects of trauma. There may not be a factor more powerful than parental love itself that can prepare an individual for life's painful tests. Collectively all of these factors are much like the emotional equivalent of suiting up with a knight's armor before encountering demons and dragons. They comprise a recipe that greatly enhances a person's ability to bounce back, to be resilient.

But what about the person who can't settle for that? What can be done for the person who insists on striving for a more robust response to trauma, the person who wants to thrive and flourish? An optimistic exploration of post-traumatic growth theories follows in chapter 3.

Our bodies know they belong; it is our minds that make our lives so homeless.

—JOHN O'DONAHUE

Good sailors are not made on calm seas.

—AFRICAN PROVERB

THREE

Post-Traumatic Growth

One heals suffering only by experiencing it to the full.

—Marcel Proust

Today PTSD no longer needs to be seen as an intractable final and fateful destiny where victims will remain stuck, languishing in discomfort for years. For the majority of people it is a momentary stopping point on a much longer and often grand journey. The reality of recovery is in acknowledging it happened, finding its meaning without trying to jettison the experience from life by denial or other means (integration), and going on with life better than before as a result of the experience (flourishing). Trauma is now seen as an engine of transformation, a springboard or catalyst for growth. After a severe adversity some people experience what Maslow referred to as a *peak experience*, when deep feelings of peace and interconnectedness overtake them. It is like they have had a sudden epiphany, when everything in life is much more understandable and their outlook is far more encouraging.

The new pioneers of trauma do not discount or minimize the frightening nature of trauma, including the painful and even near-death experiences that many people have undergone. They are not suggesting victims should be naïvely cheerful in the face of overwhelming calamities. However, many psychologists regard the aftermath of trauma as a somewhat normal chain of events, albeit a painful part of life—stressors that are, more often than not, transient in nature. Post-trauma symptoms frequently diminish over time and very often disappear after responsive interventions have been applied. This new and more optimistic psychology of trauma doesn't suggest the elimination of the PTSD paradigm. The phenomenon of PTSD is very real and belongs on a dynamic continuum between trauma itself and post-traumatic growth.

Trauma → Post-Traumatic Stress Disorder → Post-Traumatic Growth → Positive Integration

Scary times are supposed to generate anxiety and sleeplessness, but for variable and limited periods of time depending upon a victim's response to them. It should be acknowledged that sad events are supposed to yield unhappy moods or even depression, but for limited and variable periods of time. Unpleasant traumatic images may persist and naturally bleed over into reality, but for limited and varying periods of time. Uncontrollable circumstances can shake a person's foundation and create unease and uncertainty, but for limited and varying periods of time. A benevolent worldview can be momentarily shattered by traumatic experiences causing some people to distrust others; this is highly variable too, depending on an individual's response to the situation. How people cognitively and behaviorally relate to difficult events will help determine the speed, trajectory, and range of their recovery. A degree of personal influence over disquieting events is always possible. Victims are not locked into a mechanical and unalterable clockwork model of traumatic sequelae. Yet healing professionals are embedded in a uniquely Western worldview that is disinclined to see feelings of pain, sadness, or suffering as emotions that can be embraced and understood for their eventual benefits. As Greenspan (2003, 121) reflected in *Healing Through the Dark Moments,* "Prior to the advent of modern psychology, despair was an expected part of the human condition." Previously we had few choices other than to learn how to sit with it, ride it out, and resultantly develop a "muscular faith" in our innate resiliency. Now we are inclined, and even encouraged by advertising, to avoid even brief encounters with emotional discomfort. Only infrequently does our culture recognize and discuss the value of pain, the gifts hidden in suffering, the meaning buried in tragedies, or the transformative power of trauma. I can't help but recall the words of Carl Jung who concluded, "All neurosis is a substitute for legitimate suffering."

Because the vast majority of people will experience one or more traumatic events in their lives, we should be fortified in the knowledge that only about 7 or 8 percent of people react in a way that merits a PTSD diagnosis (Joseph 2011). Most people have an innate ability to recover and even thrive, especially when embedded in a compassionate support network. Creative and flexible thinking, matched with innovative counseling, can transport them into a new and stronger place. These are hallmarks of post-traumatic growth (PTG) and a post-traumatic thriving response (PTTR).

Post-Traumatic Growth (PTG) and
Post-Traumatic Thriving Response (PTTR)

The notion that positive changes can occur in the aftermath of crisis defines PTG and PTTR. The term *post-traumatic growth* was coined by Tedeschi and Calhoun in 1998. Similar conceptualizations have arisen since then including *stress-induced growth (SIG)*, *post-traumatic thriving response (PTTR)*, and *suffering-induced transformational experiences (SITEs)*. Again and again, research is revealing how not only is it common for individuals to bounce back to their pre-trauma health (resiliency), but it is also very common for victims to grow because of trauma and to develop previously unforeseen and never before experienced strengths (thriving). Studies now show that it is very much a part of our human nature to surmount psychological adversities, to leap forward, and rise above prior levels of functioning—to actually flourish. Researchers are now discovering how to awaken forgotten abilities in humans. Similar to what is observed in the rest of the animal world we can become reacquainted with atrophied qualities within our species, talents that once helped us to overcome ancient challenges.

The professional literature has documented a variety of terms to describe how people can react to trauma. *Coping* (Lazarus 1984) is a process model of trauma response. It describes an elementary and somewhat interactive (vs. automatic) way of responding, that asserts individuals have what it takes to adjust to or get past trauma. Similar to *surviving*, coping can be placed one level above passive *suffering*, two steps above *surrendering* or *succumbing*, and is far more desirable than *kindling* (when agony remains unchallenged and slumbers interminably but frequently is awakened by triggers that resemble the original trauma). For the most part these are *avoidance-oriented* ways of coping. Increasingly effective *approach-oriented* strategies engage trauma directly with the victims being more inclined to "mix it up" with painful emotions.

A critical factor that separates persons who languish in suffering from those who heal and move on to a better life has to do with their *inner locus of control*. Because trauma is usually caused by external phenomenon that can leave a person feeling weakened, at least initially, for many people it erroneously follows that external factors must be sought to help them cope. Yet the individuals who recover most dramatically appear to have a very well-developed internal sense of control. They rely on the mobilization of their inner wisdom and personal resolve to get them through challenging times. While external social support is valued and useful, thrivers, as mentioned earlier, don't wait for people to arrive and rescue them. They "work the phones" and get out of the house, all the while drawing upon their own inner resources to overcome difficult times.

Many individuals dislike being labeled as a victim. Joseph (2011, 149) wrote, "Therapy is at its best when it empowers people to take responsibility for their own recovery and helps them realize that the tools necessary to undertake the journey are in their own hands." Thrivers, even in the face of fear, garner the courage to move toward traumatic memories rather than dodge and avoid them. They look trauma in the face and wrestle with it. Thrivers also resist the natural inclination to allow victimization to define them or become their primary identity (e.g., "I am a survivor of sexual abuse"). Their way of responding to adversity eventually becomes a mark of their strong character. My maternal grandmother used to call this quality "spunk."

PTG and similar flourishing paradigms refer to a healing, strengthening, or steeling response that often follows severe stress or adversity. It validates some of the best features of our human nature: that we can be raised up, improved, elevated, and become more joyful as a result of trauma. As one of my patients described it, PTG is about moving with and through difficult times, about "flowing into growing." It often entails the element of *savoring*, spending time with suffering to learn as much as possible from the experience. Savoring is about being greedy in the best sense of the word, meaning a person refuses to let a painful event come and go without wringing out of it all the inherent insights and teachings held in the trauma. Savoring implies that growth comes from fully experiencing not only discomfort and sorrow but also the care, support, and joy that often follow crises, especially after friends have stepped forward to offer attentive and loving kindness. When a person notices all sides of trauma including its positive factors, it is common to experience a renewal of hope, trust, and faith in humankind. With that recognition a renewed vitality and altruism develop. Trauma doesn't force them to resign into a state of despair, cynicism, and isolation. It often reconnects sufferers in deeper ways with some of the best people around them. After a trauma experience, thrivers will likely conclude more strongly than ever, "I'm not alone," in part because they successfully summoned a helpful support network to their side, but also because a general sense of unity and connection permeates them.

Positive psychology, humanistic psychology, and Buddhist psychology influences are at the vanguard of this new/old movement that blends traditional yet cutting-edge ways of viewing persistent emotional maladies. Depression, for example, is no longer perceived as a medical event that requires an exclusively biochemical eradication plan. The existence of a biochemical substrate to an uncomfortable emotional state like depression is not proof that pharmacological intervention is required. The immediate and pervasive manner by which Americans diagnose and treat depression may reflect how much our culture fears and devalues despair, regarding it as uniformly harmful and unnecessary, something that must be nipped in the bud. And advertisements that suggest it should be treated from a strictly pathological paradigm lower our tolerance for negative affect and extended sadness. The history of the human species has shown that depression is a tolerable condition, it often spurs hardiness and growth, and it has likely done so for the last 70,000 years of *Homo sapiens'* existence prior to the advent of the modern antidepressant era beginning in the 1970s. Ancient wisdom, in contrast, portrays fear and depression as unalchemized despair. Despair's messages are both a call to re-examination of our life's meaning and a call to transformation. Sometimes drugs can blunt or cloud nature's clarifying messages that arise from fear.

As Mark Twain said in his typically concise way, "Courage is mastery of fear, not absence of fear." And mastery doesn't have to look like a struggle or a war. It usually enlists a quieter strategy to tame fear. In fact, when victims fight or resist their once fear-filled past, it may linger and carry over to the present. As Carl Jung clarified, "What we resist, will persist."

PTSD patients can become unconsciously addicted to their problems, even addicted to misery and unhappiness. They recreate patterns that are well known even though it keeps life unpleasant. In large part this is because a life of survivable familiarity feels somewhat safe. A certain measure of unhappiness is "required" to maintain inner equilibrium. And ongoing sadness may be in keeping with a trauma-generated belief from long ago that suggests this is all I deserve (Pieper and Pieper 2003). Similarly, many victims of trauma become deeply attached (addicted) to their life narrative, their painful story of what should not have happened to them. Often they will obsess and ruminate on a feeling state (an addictive process), thereby keeping it robust. The primary addiction is to their thinking and to an attendant emotional state at the time (Prendergast et al. 2003). All of this, while serving an immediate survival purpose, thwarts long-term movement toward post-traumatic growth.

Ancient wisdom traditions have been shown to be quite rewarding and effective in treating PTSD. At first glance, they may appear passive and confusing, as if depressives are being encouraged to simply resign themselves to being bystanders. Buddhist psychology literature refers to a discerning approach strategy called "the way of non-action"; it is a courageous observational period when the trauma victims muster the strength to sit with their sadness and fear. They are encouraged to ride out their depression by engaging in *emotional surfing*, trusting that like powerful ocean waves, strong feelings eventually dissipate, as in the case of the waves when they come ashore. Thrivers ride waves of emotion like a surfer, mindfully observing what is happening from a perspective slightly above the turmoil. Their task is simply to be present with emotions of vulnerability, not acquiescing, running, medicating, fixing, or doing battle with them. They become increasingly more comfortable holding the tension of the moment, not feeling compelled to resolve it too quickly. This is a thoughtful strategy about "letting life be" by not denying reality, while at the same time, attending to fear and allowing it to become an alchemical gateway to joy.

It has been said many times that life brings pain. That is guaranteed. Then the caveat is sometimes added, which posits that ongoing suffering may be optional. Pain is that acute "ouch," the physical or emotional hurt we experience when someone betrays us, punches us, steals from us. And suffering, to me, is the default state our minds fall into when we are not paying close attention to what is happening, when we have drifted out of the moment. Suffering is what happens in our cognitive default state when we almost automatically engage in negativity, grumbling, complaining, and judging. It becomes the lingering background noise of our own creation. So, it is what we do with and after painful events that determines the extent and duration of suffering that follows. Do we obsess on the trauma and plot a satisfying retaliation, or seek a higher road as a result of the pain? In other words, do we join ranks with the perpetrator and live by a mutual credo, "Hurt people, hurt people," or do we ask ourselves, "Is he teaching me how not to be?" The first question keeps suffering alive, the second transmutes it into something positive.

In some Native American cultures a death is followed by a year-long grieving period for the surviving spouse or family members. This implies that overcoming sadness is not always quick and easy, that pain is an eminently human emotion that has a somewhat predictable shelf life. They believe that if individuals are willing to notice it, endure it, and be strengthened by it, depression and despair will also pass away, often leaving the bereaved stronger and wiser for the wear. And, of course, this often comes while the depressive is held in the embrace of a tightly knit community of support. What I am explaining is more than just speculative philosophy or theory. It is ancient wisdom that is now being resuscitated by a society that is growing wary of one-dimensional cures. Part of this wisdom proposes that life has shadows, thanks to a shining sun. Or as Leonard Cohen wrote in "Anthem," "There's a crack in everything; that's how the light gets in." Trauma can break people's hearts, but it can also crack them open to a wiser and richer heartfelt existence.

SITEs Research

Recent research is uncovering the benefits of this new/old way of posturing oneself toward trauma. A United Kingdom study (Taylor 2012) of 32 persons who underwent periods of intense trauma and stress in their lives (bereavement, serious illnesses, depression, disability, alcoholism, and/or near-death experiences) found the majority, 24 persons, reported very similar and positive transformations afterward. Rather than undergo a regression of psychological health, the individuals studied displayed a post-trauma progression, advancing to psychological states in which they were remarkably free of intra- and interpersonal discord. Even more encouraging was how most everyone described their psychological metamorphosis as spiritually enriching and, generally, long-lasting in nature.

Stanislov Grof (2000) characterized extraordinarily challenging periods as *spiritual emergencies,* times when our foundational beliefs are shaken to the core leaving us irrevocably changed, often for the better. Merton (2004) wrote about *dark nights of the soul,* those disquieting, extended, and profoundly sad periods when lives cease to have meaning and previous beliefs and values are thrown into question. The SITEs respondents underwent similar kinds of experiences but came out the other side more optimistic and happier than before. Some of the most common positive changes observed after their tragedies included:

- Feeling less selfish, more altruistic, and increasingly empathetic
- Improved social relationships; a greater sense of connectedness and compassion
- More fulfilling life; a greater sense of well-being
- A new sense of purpose and meaning, as well as new values that grew from the traumas
- Feeling reborn, as if finally an authentic self
- New, more positive personal identities
- Increased comfort during times of solitude, without becoming defensively isolative

- A dramatic reduction of egoic consciousness, plus a vastly broadened sense of unity, not just with people but with the entire cosmos
- Greater mental clarity; the world, even with all its suffering, suddenly made sense to them
- Living more in the moment, rather than in depressive sadness reliving the past, or in apprehension and worry over the future
- A diminished fear of death
- Feeling spiritually awakened
- A religious conversion or moving away from the acceptance of many prior dogmas; relinquishing old beliefs and concepts because that felt too confining and restrictive
- Feelings of self-actualization

Mechanisms of Transformation

So what are the elements that can germinate transformative break-throughs rather than cause degenerative breakdowns? Taylor (2012) hypothesized that massive anxiety or stress resulting from trauma can reach a peak of intensity when the psyche suddenly dissolves. The old psychological term *decompensation* doesn't really fit here because of its predominantly negative connotations. Instead of collapsing into a psychotic break, SITEs respondents remained present throughout their extraordinarily painful periods of instability and confusion, and eventually broke through to a level of clarity never before known to them. An unfolding thriving process apparently occurred when the psyche's old exoskeleton of beliefs could no longer maintain itself in the face of powerfully new, unsettling, and dramatic experiences. A vacuum was created as old beliefs were shattered and fell away. Relief and contentment remained leaving some of the thrivers in a satisfying state of suspension, nebulousness, and mystery. Rather than feeling lost and naked, SITEs reported feeling liberated. In essence, old cherished attachments were broken or dissolved, ones that in hindsight had never served the individual very well in the first place. Cataclysmic events served to violently "rock the boat" and scramble old notions, including worldviews that had been unchallenged for far too long and provided only limited coping power. Once the trauma victims detached from and surrendered to their experience, acceptance and integration were possible. They were touched by the light of darkness.

Talking About Trauma

Some psychological theorists contend that through avoidance (not thinking or talking about a traumatic event) the potential for positive transformation is reduced (Lancaster and Palframan 2009). Over the years most psychotherapists have concluded that an *abreactive* approach, that involved discharging strong negative emotions and thoroughly discussing the traumatic experiences, was integral to recovery. Rather than examine this question in dichotomous terms (avoid or vent) it may be more helpful to ask when it is helpful to recall a trauma and when it is appropriate to nudge it out of the mind.

PTG can unfold in somewhat complex and counterintuitive ways. For the process to get under way usually it is valuable to tell the story of the actual facts surrounding the trauma without an *awfulizing* editorial quality, and then to explain how the victim plans to address the experiences thereafter. This entails a brave, active, and accurate confrontation of memories, when a person marshals the courage to approach and revisit painful events. As the residual effects of the tragic experience abate, along with some of its riveting distractions and/or attendant dissociation, obstructions are removed that allow for increased mental clarity, thereby enabling recovery and growth to begin. When the tumultuous circumstances have ceased, it is time to remember and reflect, to assess and make sense of what has happened—both the damage that was done and the potential development that awaits. It is a time for the patient and therapist to be careful to tell only a factual story of the trauma that will lay a foundation from which realistic interpretations can later be drawn.

Weeks, months, or years later a restorying can occur, outlining new places that the now historical trauma can take the victim. Through the restorying process patients can imagine the possibilities that now await them. Even before restorying a trauma, simply entertaining the *willingness* to one day do that kind of work has been shown to have a healing effect on the brain (McGonigal 2012). Creating a new story, post-trauma, results in a continuous reminder that a painful period may be fading into the past. While it is not settled yet, there is some cognitive movement. New vistas are being imaged, and this mental activity heals the brain too. Even unrealistic fantasies can have a healing power as they give the *mindbody* a break from all the previous degenerative negativity, supplanting the recall of unpleasant memories with a new emotional coloring. (More on this in chapter 6.)

Sometimes, and often quite counterintuitively, growth occurs when victims periodically avoid thinking or talking about their problems, they choose not to recount what happened to them. Wickelgren (2012) contends that discreetly holding back and suppressing painful thoughts, in contrast with repeated venting, can be healing too. This process can help quiet the amygdala, the trauma-activated fear center of the brain that resides adjacent to the neighboring hippocampus region, which is the memory center that records unpleasant emotions and attendant images from right next door. Frequently replayed memories may not benefit victims because they become deeply etched into the brain. They cut grooves that later may spring up uncontrollably, even years later in the form of invasive images or flashbacks triggered by stimuli that resemble (even vaguely) events of the past. So, early in recovery the quieting and healing periods in this deep brain region may prove valuable, especially for victims who were highly anxious individuals to begin with. The mental recesses can lay the groundwork for *neuroplasticity,* a healing reconfiguration of the brain's neuro-circuitry.

To initiate a patient's recovery it isn't necessary to immediately jump right into remembering and revealing horrible events. Psychologist Paul Pearsall (2003) suggests using the talent of a "healthy forgettory." He describes it as the counterpart to memory that intuitively knows when to talk and reflect, and when to move on, as opposed to continuously ruminating about historical things that a person cannot erase. By consciously slowing down amygdala over-activity and agitation through healthy forgetting, the brain acts as if a fuse has momentarily been blown. It disrupts the natural transfer of frightening information into hippocampal memory while providing a vital and restorative break from stress. This "timeout" halts what is referred to as a *stress-induced fear circuitry disorder,* a problem of chronic hypervigilence that often presents like a severe anxiety disorder. PTSD signifies there has been a problem of insufficient or inefficient forgetting, a person has temporarily lost the ability to titrate the recall of unpleasant information thereby allowing it to become overwhelming and flood consciousness. PTG recovery, in contrast, is about remembering a bit, "forgetting" a bit, and working it through at the strongest and most opportune times. It is about knowing when to hit the brain's "delete" key. Even knowing when it is wise to momentarily "give up." Thrivers seem to know how to disengage for a time, engage in intentional and selective denying, and practice elective quitting or thoughtful disengagement (partial dissociation), all of which are helpful to the PTG process. Having the courage to confront pain, and the knowledge of when to take a break from facing it, should all be guided by a PTG therapist.

Then there is the matter of long-term memory, the intentional recall of information of how they previously saved themselves. It can be a difficult task amid the stress of a current tragedy when the amygdala is hyperactive and overrides logical and linear thinking. This dilemma points to the importance of having journaled about one's strengths in the past so the evidence can later be recovered and used as needed. Written accounts can prompt the recall of old patient memories, which can be downloaded months or years later, proof positive that they had, and still have, what it takes to get through a traumatic period. Prefrontal activation with its logical and insightful input may not occur during a crisis without being stimulated by some kind of external aid, like a journal or an old therapist who has walked down this road with them before.

Over and over again psychological literature has referred to two additional factors that are linked to PTG and PTTR. They are a *salutogenic orientation* (Antonovsky 1987) and a *flexible explanatory style* (Pearsall 2003). Unlike some studies (e.g., ACEs research) and healthcare providers that can "hex" victims with pathogenic orientations and correlations between trauma and the eventual breakdown of health (both psychological and physical) a salutogenic orientation places the focus of attention on slumbering personal strengths. This, as we will later see, requires a language of strengths and the knowledge of assessment measures to identify them, as well as techniques to maximize their mitigating powers. So when the "cosmic alarm" of trauma sounds, it is time to ask patients, "What's right with you?" rather than only, "What's wrong with you?"

Having a *flexible explanatory style* is a slightly cumbersome way to say that certain trauma victims may have a natural adaptive talent to craft a realistically optimistic long-range outlook. They are adept at seeing things from many different angles. They have created a *dialogical space* within their mind, an ability to recognize that traumatic events don't necessarily have concrete, automatic, and fixed impacts on people. Thrivers understand self-determination and are alert to the subjective role they play in crafting a desired outcome. Often they see themselves as different from others and not necessarily narrowly scripted by unfortunate life events. By displaying sustained competence under stress and from having adaptive personality traits, each new life challenge is met with increased confidence.

I believe PTSD is a disorder of information processing, especially when the brain isn't working optimally under conditions of fear and terror. When emotions calm down, however, normal memory processing mechanisms come back online and victims can make better sense of what has happened to them, thereby moving them out of the trauma. Thrivers look like what Lyubomirsky (2001) called *good construers,* individuals who engage their problems adaptively and adjust their perspective in ways that make them more psychologically immune to later stressors. They flow with life and its adversities. Cognitive psychologists refer to flexible explanatory styles as an individual's unique way of seeing events and assigning optimistic meaning to them. They have a knack for accurately seeing the lemonade that can be made from some mighty sour lemons. This trait was epitomized by an intellectually disabled Wyoming boy who had been sexually abused. He had an incredible talent for meticulously carving realistic images of horses out of blocks of wood. When I asked him how he was able to carve beautiful horses from the chunks of wood he said, "I just cut off the parts that are not horse." What we have come to believe we may later create. When you believe it, you can see it.

PTG is facilitated more by a process than any specific personality trait, although we will later see how specific traits can also enhance the process. It is about being creative, adaptive, flexible, open, responsive, and capable of flowing with life amid all its sunshine as well as its frequent storms. Thrivers, or as some people call them, "invincibles," engage in a fluid dance with life, flinching and then yielding to unexpected vicissitudes. They can change their posture and attitude to fit whatever challenging occasion confronts them. Like a supple tree, they bend and twist, but rarely break. They know when it is best to laugh in the face of danger and when to take cover, not being bound by any one-size-fits-all approach to life.

Sometimes they are inclined to practice forgiveness but my sense of it is that thrivers forgive in a very enlightened way. They think of forgiveness in terms of the literal Greek meaning: untying a knot. Forgiveness is a process whereby you break an unhealthy connection, you let go of the toxic bond that once existed between yourself and the abuser. It is a way of saying, "I no longer hold you responsible for how I feel today. I'm moving on." Seen through this lens, forgiveness is an empowering posture that offers a fresh start, breaking the shackles of a previously burdensome relationship.

Joseph (2011), in his book *What Doesn't Kill Us,* posits there are three existential themes at the core of PTG. *First,* a person who is harmed by trauma and yet is inclined to grow from it recognizes that life is unpredictable, that events are constantly changing. It follows the Buddhist teaching: Life brings suffering, or as teenagers will bluntly say, "Shit happens." Recognizing and recalling these basic truths takes some of the surprise away from life's inevitable tragedies; they no longer blindside us with as much force. *Second,* psychological mindfulness exemplified by a flexible attitude toward change, sets the stage for growth. Trauma may force victims to configure a new and much-needed alternative perspective toward life. An adaptive attitude certainly helps to move many people in the direction of PTG. *Third,* the acknowledgment of personal agency or an inner locus of control (a sense of personal responsibility for the choices one makes) helps people tame the negative and harness the positive energy of traumatic experiences.

Some of the really tough stuff in life, physical and sexual traumas, deaths, devastating natural events, and other horrifying experiences, can become profound teachers. They hold the potential to stretch people into new ways of being, to expand perspectives, to awaken hidden talents, and to enlarge empathy and compassion for others. Martin Luther King Jr. used to talk about suffering as a "creative force," suggesting it holds an energy that can be transmuted into something good.

Personal, Familial, and Cultural Supports for PTG

How parents talk to their children about painful life tests can help youngsters imagine positive outcomes before the inevitable difficult times arrive. When parents speak from wise, experienced, and profoundly tested backgrounds, seeds of hope and resiliency are planted in young, developing minds. In this way parents *lend ego* until children have sufficient strength to stand on their own. Furthermore, springing from the intimacy with their children, parents set up a collective resonance affect, a brain entrainment response, whereby their kids attune themselves to the spirit of the loving adults surrounding them. This synchrony is now explained by science. Just as neurons that fire together wire together, people who fire together wire together. In a very real way, there is healing strength in numbers (McTaggart 2011). The power of a coherent group of friends or loved ones can override individual limitations (Cohen et al. 2010).

A survey of professional literature on PTG has yielded a lengthy and very helpful list of factors than have been correlated with this healing paradigm. How victims respond to and process trauma is of utmost importance, more than the nature or severity of the events themselves. Certain personality traits and life circumstances tend to be important too. What follows are some of the ingredients required for a PTG recovery recipe. If you are supporting someone who has been harmed by an unexpected and highly stressful event, if that person was terrorized and felt his or her life was threatened, search for and reinforce these elements as you organize and orchestrate a treatment plan.

- Consistent family support and positive connections, plus the capacity to build mutual caring relationships with others, has been shown to foster growth.
- Assembling a guiding core of inner personally developed spiritual beliefs can aid recovery.
- Good self-esteem (self-worth and self-confidence), a strong inner locus of control, and proper attribution of responsibility for the trauma are correlated with positive change.
- A commitment to reflection, holding flexible problem solving skills, having the ability to think in psychologically minded ways, and having a knack for finding positive meaning in negative events aids recovery.
- Having an array of self-care strategies and routines for managing painful, negative, and overwhelming affect in place is significantly helpful.
- When a person strives to be an actor and not just a reactor, this proactive stance is inclined to advance recovery.
- The ability to assert the right to having one's own needs met, and to set limits in relationships, aids recovery.
- The persistent determination to adjust, matched with a belief in realistic societal messages of hope, makes a difference.
- The knowledge that perpetrators of hurt and harm likely had negative experiences and influences in their own lives often helps victims depersonalize painful events.
- A timely resumption of life is important. For example, getting back on the horse after a fall, going back to the wilderness after a grizzly bear encounter, when prudently done can hasten recovery and build inner strength.
- Being intelligent and humorous helps too.
- Breaking secrecy is important. The more actively a trauma is processed (not just relived and lamented in the same way each time) the better chance one has for growth and a successful recovery.

- A sense of accomplishment and efficacy in other non-trauma areas of life helps recovery from painful events go better.
- Joining with others in groups (where there is more than a continuous retelling of abuses and the reinforcement of a victim identity) lends support.
- Positive corrective relationships with members of the opposite sex help victims who were abused by members of the opposite sex recover more completely.
- Telling a creative story (*reauthoring* or *restorying*) about the trauma and the plan for recovery helps to describe and then create the victim's future. The process has more power than the trauma itself to define the victim. Traumatic events matter far less than the victorious stories wrapped around them.
- Affixing meaning and a sense of purpose to traumatic experiences dramatically increases the chance for post-traumatic growth, integration, and successful resolution.

Condensing Judith Herman's (1992) theory, there is a 3-stage process to trauma recovery: 1) establishing safety; 2) remembrance and mourning; and 3) reconnection. I suggest some minor tweaking to suggest what may work best for our patients is a remembrance *with meaning* and a *purposeful connectedness,* namely being in the company of other like-minded individuals who are joined in a mission to improve some part of society. With those elements in place the harvest of hope can begin in earnest.

Finally, a few very important **words of caution**. As therapists, our enthusiasm for PTG must be tamped down at times. To push a positive and transformative healing paradigm too early in the therapy process can have deleterious effects. Until Herman's first two stages have been adequately visited, applying PTG theory prematurely can be experienced as colluding in a process of minimization or denial, as though the trauma was not a big deal. As patients grow in their ability to sit for a time with their pain, helping professionals must be willing to do the same. Patients will move ahead on their own timetable. When we notice a time when patients show some initial movement toward meaning, connection, integration, or transformation, our task at that time is simply to shine a light on their accomplishments and exhort them onward. PTG happens at the patient's pace. Trauma patients can't be pushed or controlled. Being pushed by one's therapist can easily feel like an additional loss of power. Our most important therapeutic tasks are to create safety, hold sacred space, and provide timely encouragement.

In chapter 4, we will move from recovery theory to the application of pragmatic techniques and exercises, recalling that our compassionate therapeutic presence will carry the day more than any treatment modality.

Sweet are the uses of adversity,
Which like the toad, ugly and venomous,
Wears a precious jewel in his head.

—WILLIAM SHAKESPEARE

FOUR

Sexual Abuse Recovery

To the extent that we hold on to a no-longer-existent past,
we are not available for the unfolding present.

—KAREN KISSEL WEGELA in *The Courage to Be Present*

A traumatic event, by itself, is not inherently damaging over the long term. More often than not, what causes lasting harm is a personal history of unresolved trauma and a person's incomplete reaction to a current adversity. This supposition is not intended as a way to blame victims for their pain and suffering, rather it is a way of suggesting that the ability to bounce back, or better said, bounce forward, following a painful event largely rests in the victims' minds, how they choose to respond and relate (not just react) to adversity. When a person is harmed, that person—not the perpetrator, law enforcement, therapists, or the courts—has the greatest power and ability to influence the eventual outcome. The meaning-makers, the cognitively flexible individuals, who are surrounded by compassionate and dependable friends, are most likely to recover expeditiously. This applies to all kinds of trauma, including sexual abuse.

Sexual abuse trauma has certain features that set it apart from other less personal adversities like being the victim of a flood, a tornado, an explosion, a plane crash, being diagnosed with cancer, or experiencing the sudden loss of a loved one to an unexpected disease. Sexual abuse is somewhat unique in that it is regarded as a *betrayal trauma* (Freyd 1996). When a person is randomly chosen, or even groomed to be the target of a sex crime, there is a person-to-person dynamic that almost uniformly leaves the victim asking the proverbial questions, "Why me?" or, "What did I do to deserve this?" Because the majority of sexual abuse cases are committed by someone known to the victim, it follows that those who are harmed may question their own judgment for socializing with the assailant. And if their bodies responded in a natural way to sexual touch and some pleasure was experienced, it isn't uncommon to ask "What is wrong with me?" Sometimes the body becomes as much of an enemy as the actual perpetrator and is punished with eating disorders, self-mutilation, or by acting out sexually.

To understand the uniqueness of sexual abuse sequelae it is helpful to apply the *traumagenic dynamics* as first formulated by David Finkelhor (1986). He postulated that the impact of sexual abuse can be assessed in four primary areas: *betrayal, powerlessness, stigmatization,* and *sexual traumatization.* The first three dynamics are of an interpersonal or intrapersonal nature, whereas the fourth may have an additional impact inherent to the qualities of the traumatic acts themselves. Each dynamic can be uniquely encoded by the victim in a way that personalizes and distorts the event. Therefore it is important for therapists to assist in accurately processing the trauma, accurately attributing responsibility, and accurately interpreting what constitutes a normal (vs. abnormal) reaction to a set of abnormal events.

Betrayal may be the most powerful traumagenic dynamic as it goes to the core of who we can trust and if we can feel safe in this world. Deception, trickery, manipulation, bribery, false reassurances, broken promises, seduction, lack of parental protection, and carefully developed dependency can give rise to a sense of betrayal. Feinauer, in Freyd (1989), argues that the most devastating psychological effects of childhood sexual abuse can occur when the abuser is someone known and trusted by the child or the child's family. If the last bastion of safety, the family home, happens to be where the perpetrator lives and commits the abuse, a child may be denied a foundation of security to rest on. Normally it is from a solid basis of trust in a secure family home that children can successfully extend themselves in social ways and safely engage with others in their community. When core trust is violated and therefore absent, therapists are often called upon to fill the emotional void by being a steady and protective parent-like figure in the victim's life. To have a corrective presence, all mental health providers (doctors, counselors, foster parents, advocates, etc.) must model dependability, predictability, and reasonable availability. If a patient has a 2 p.m. appointment with us we must be reliably available at 2 p.m., not 2:15. Similarly, we must avoid canceling appointments except under the most urgent situations because healing the victim of sexual abuse requires an unvarying presence from us. Counseling rituals may serve to anchor the patient in a comforting healing routine. It is also important not to promise outcomes that are beyond our control. For example, to reassure a victim that the legal system will find a perpetrator guilty, and that a just and corrective sentence will be administered, could prove untrue and may be experienced as an additional form of betrayal and another tier of vicitimization, especially when coming from a person perceived as a fountainhead of reliability like a judge, physician, or a social worker.

When a victim's body is stimulated and comes alive during an assault experience, and when it responds with natural signs of arousal, it may seem like an internal betrayal has occurred. It is one thing to have outsiders let us down, but our own bodies too? When an assault occurs, particularly when it is very distressing and frightening, humans (and other animals) are inclined to dissociate, to mentally "go away," and enter a trance for safety. Victims cannot apply normal morality when their analytical brains are shut down in self-protection mode. Meanwhile, without a governing mind at work, the body is left on automatic pilot to operate normally, thus when sexually stimulated the body reacts by lubricating, engorging sexual organs with blood, feeling pleasure, or having an orgasm. One way to interpret this reaction is to reassure patients that their body was not broken by the experience; it still operated as designed by nature. No repair work will be needed. Thanks to the adaptive response of dissociation, both body and mind were protected to a degree. To refer to dissociation as a "disorder" when it occurs under these extreme circumstances could be an egregious mistake. It is usually more accurate to regard this protective reaction as nature's way of protecting people, especially under very threatening circumstances.

Powerlessness, which is typically experienced during and after an assault, can leave the victim of sexual abuse feeling helpless, like a leaf twisting and turning in the wind. Powerlessness can manifest as anxiety, panic, insomnia, nightmares, OCD, dissociation, delinquency, and in wide variety of controlling ways including abuse-reactive or sexually assaultive behavior. The victims may have felt powerless when they froze, when they couldn't stop the assault, when they couldn't convince others that it happened, when a parent failed to protect them, or when the legal system seemed unresponsive.

Being over-controlling in relationships may feel like a compensatory attempt to find safety, but it can come at the expense of pushing a good partner away. Common thinking is, "If I can control his/her behavior, I won't get hurt." It may not feel quite right at the time, usually because the control gets mislabeled as something else, perhaps as love. Control may be portrayed as concern for the other, but is actually quite self-focused and singularly protective. Ultimately, when control is intended to restrain another person to guarantee a safe and enduring relationship, it may yield the opposite result and not uncommonly the partner bolts. A therapist can, in a very face-saving way for patients, assist them in examining, understanding, and owning this choice. There isn't a question of right or wrong that needs to be confronted, just a question about the effectiveness of an attempted solution. When patients become increasingly more aware and more effective in all that they do, they grow in power, and enhance their self-esteem as well.

The therapeutic task is to empower sexual abuse patients at every turn. They can be empowered by meeting with a prosecutor before charges are brought or before a trial begins. Empowerment occurs when they actively choose a counselor who is best suited for them or by providing input into the length, frequency, or content of therapy sessions. Empowerment comes from learning assertion skills, by being included in a healthy support group, through involvement in a restorative justice healing circle, by having the final word about what medications (if any) enter their bodies, or by learning how to manage anxiety. Empowerment is also about putting wheels on their beliefs, by helping them live out their convictions.

It is possible that an abuse experience will provide significant personal challenges that, once conquered, leave the victim feeling stronger and more confident than ever before. Following the resolution and integration of a tragic situation, victims are often endowed with a humble but strong inner authority. Their still, small voice, as Quakers might call it, now has an authoritative tone to it. When a therapist notes these signs of individual efficacy developing, it is important to call attention to them, thereby reinforcing the change.

Alpha-Stim microcurrent brain stimulation is a remarkably effective and efficient way to regulate the perturbation of anxiety and the immobilization of depression, especially during the acute stages of a trauma. This handheld device, which is FDA approved, sends tiny currents (.5 Hz) of electricity through the earlobes and into the brain. Health-care providers can purchase units to augment their counseling practice. It is not uncommon for sexual abuse victims who are consumed with anxiety and sadness to experience a profound dissipation of unpleasant symptoms within 20–30 minutes of their first Alpha-Stim treatment. Few, if any, techniques developed for the resolution of fear, panic, nervousness, insomnia, and depression are as safe, pleasant, and effective as the application of alpha-wave activity to an upset brain, specifically the deep limbic region that includes the amygdala and the basal ganglia, where fear and anxiety originate. Patients can be taught how to self-administer treatments at home using a compact microcurrent stimulation device. This technique has been shown to be immensely helpful in the empowerment process.

Another way to bring calming empowerment into lives of past victims is by the use of Eye Movement Desensitization and Reintegration (EMDR) and similar treatments like *Brainspotting*. It isn't uncommon for victims to experience peace and acceptance around their abusive experiences after only four to six EMDR sessions, sometimes complimented with tapping techniques. While the techniques and protocols (rituals) are valuable by themselves, a safe and reassuring relationship with a warm and attentive clinician is every bit as important. Loving kindness is the best antidote to interpersonal exploitation.

We can never remind victims of sexual abuse often enough that they have a choice of who will provide supportive services and how they will be provided. They must be the chairpersons of their healing wellness programs. Our responsibility is not to just organize a treatment plan and advise them, but more importantly, to serve them in ways of their choice.

Stigmatization occurs when sexual trauma leaves a victim feeling dirty, unclean, defiled, flawed, or contaminated. Sexual abuse is an assault not only on the body, but on a person's self-esteem as well. It is never prudent to argue with victims about what they feel. Feelings are not right or wrong, they just are. Like all things in life, feelings tend to be impermanent; they will change and pass over time. During treatment therapists may simply ask victims of sexual abuse to observe unpleasant feelings as they quite naturally ebb and flow, to surf them while noting their diminishing shelf life. Additionally, have them take note of the chosen strategies that may have hastened the dissipation of unpleasant emotions. We want them to feel good about themselves and empowered by their own choices and abilities.

It is vitally important that therapists constantly monitor their word choice, including diagnostic terminology that, while appearing benign to us, may be experienced as pathologizing to a sexual assault victim. Diagnostic terms suggesting that the victim suffers from *histrionic personality disorder, dissociative disorder, borderline personality disorder, post-traumatic stress disorder,* or even an *affective disorder* represent an insidious language of breakage. Again and again, it is the therapist's responsibility to help interpret what are expected and normal reactions to unexpected and abnormal life events. Many strong reactions are to be expected and can be a sign of health. To feel sad or depressed following sad and thoroughly disappointing events makes sense. We should expect victims to feel anxious or afraid after being scared or terrorized. It is healthy to feel anger after a personal injustice has occurred. It could be dangerous for a victim *not* to feel these emotions. Furthermore, it is important to distinguish between who has the mental health problem and who does not. Are the victim's predictable reactions to terror or harm abnormal, or would it be better to label the cruel and exploitive behaviors of the perpetrator as abnormal?

Proper attribution of blame and responsibility is important, but not when it is delivered before its time. When victims hear that they are without blame, or are actually quite healthy, while early in their recovery process, surprisingly it can generate resistance. At the beginning of counseling it may simply convince patients that their therapist is naïve, wearing rose-colored glasses, or simply being a mindless cheerleader. This type of information must be delivered in a timely fashion, titrated in amounts that are digestible for the victim, even when the conclusions are abundantly clear to us, the helpers.

Stigmatization may feel to vicitms like they have lost some of their being and absorbed undesirable parts of the abuser. Indigenous cultures call it *soul loss* or *soul theft* when long-standing parts of a person are surreptitiously severed by the imposing and smothering personality of the abuser. Soul loss refers to the temporary dispossession of one's best essence—one's confidence, poise, sweetness, optimism, trust, or innocence. It is important to note that if these traits were once present, they can be retrieved. Soul retrieval healers may ask salient questions like, "What were you like one week ago, before the assault? Because that was such a short time ago, do you believe those parts can be reawakened?"

Late in his life Jung asserted how the modern world, with all its busyness, had become desacralized. We have lost sanctifying rituals and become increasingly inclined to exploit and harm each other. When someone has endured the profanity of a sexual assault and feels stigmatized as a result, therapy must provide an opposite corrective experience. This requires the skill to develop and maintain a sacred healing environment, to sacralize all parts of the process. In my book *Ancient Ways* (2011), I offered an explanation of how patient-centered rituals can lift individuals up in ways that leave them feeling worthy, beautiful, cleansed, and sanctified. Even telling one's story of abuse in a sacred setting allows warring feelings to melt away.

The story of Tessa, a patient of mine who had been sexually assaulted, exemplifies some of the problems arising from stigmatization. Tessa joined the army shortly after high school. She was raped by a fellow soldier while serving in Iraq, what we labeled as a *moral injury*. Not surprisingly she questioned her worthiness for briefly spending time, before and after the rape, with the man who had assaulted her. Tessa felt inadequate, and even somewhat complicit, for not reporting the crime immediately to military authorities. The Veterans Administration doubted that the rape could have been severe enough to merit the PTSD diagnosis that her civilian psychiatrist had rendered. Following her discharge from the army, Tessa was consistently plagued with self-esteem issues, perceiving herself as being undesirable in the eyes of all men. When a kind and well-intentioned man sent flowers after several dates with her, Tessa felt no enjoyment receiving them. The flowers didn't even appear pretty to her, almost as if they had become contaminated in her presence. It was unpleasant to be gifted in this way and Tessa wished the bouquet had never been sent to her in the first place.

In therapy, she was encouraged to confront this enigma head-on by purchasing flowers for herself, in essence engaging in a self-compassionate ritual that was not linked to men. At first Tessa was emotionally averse to the idea, yet it seemed logical to her. Much to her surprise and my own as well, she immediately went to a flower shop and helped the florist design an arrangement for herself. Intellectually, she knew that the therapeutic exercise made sense, recognizing that sometimes the way around a problem is straight through it. To Tessa's surprise not only did she enjoy her flowers, which she unapologetically put on display at home, but the blossoms seemed to last longer than flowers ever given to her by anyone else. Tessa found symbolic messages in this therapeutic exercise: She is beautiful and deserving of beautiful treatment, and it wasn't necessary to wait for someone else to treat her with great respect. The small act of purchasing flowers as a gift to self was a major catalyst in initiating Tessa's soul recovery process.

Sexual traumatization can arise from the bizarre, confounding, painful, embarrassing, twisted, or disgusting sexual acts that a victim may have endured. The acts, as interpreted by the victim, may become stored memories in the body and when they unexpectedly erupt later on they can create additional feelings of stigmatization. They may also generate a habituated revulsion so that even when very healthy sexual expression is pursued, aversive feelings still creep in. Like uninvited guests these feelings may show up at some of the most inopportune times, destroying what was unfolding as a warm and intimate sexual experience. It may feel as though an irreparable link was created between historically unpleasant sexual acts and present-day normal sexual relations. With each undesirable intrusion, the victim's sadness, anxiety, anger, and disgust may be ignited and soon the victim anticipates each and every future experience will stimulate the exact same results. A self-fulfilling prophecy starts to unfold. Negative emotions, no matter their source, commonly interfere with satisfying erotic expression, but are especially problematic when they are affixed to abusive memories.

Sometimes the victims of sexual abuse react with what psychologist Patrick Carnes (1997) termed *sexual anorexia,* an expression of sexual self-hatred evident by the obsessive avoidance of sex. Accompanying this phenomenon is a loathing of sexual body functions and sexual experiences. Sexual anorexics repeatedly say "No" to sex, to trusting, to committing, to pleasure, and to surrendering during lovemaking. Through sexual deprivation they lose another part of themselves, another instance of soul loss. When those suffering from sexual anorexia fight back by deciding to *make* sex satisfying for them, satisfaction becomes more elusive. In response to past abuse, re-occurring desires for sex become terrifying. As Carnes explains it, people engaging in sexual anorexia tend to be plagued with shame and consequently erect "concrete walls" around their sexuality. The consequence of giving in and enjoying sex makes them feel devalued. Because of the traumatizing and stigmatizing effect of their abuse, victims feel unworthy and unlovable in most all sexual ways.

For some survivors of sexual trauma there is a pattern of processing sexual information in the extremes. During one period in life a victim may cope by avoidance. Another time may be characterized by periods of sexual binging. The same person may alternate between being shut down to periods of high-risk sexual arousal that begin to resemble a sexual addiction. *Sexual bulimia* and sexual anorexia are two sides of the same coin: both being subconscious obsessions with unresolved sexual matters. Sex has temporarily lost its playful, soothing, and intimate dimensions as a result of the consuming and confusing messages arising from abuse.

Recommending self-pleasuring sexual activities are a medium- to late-stage therapeutic measure. Before that, victims of sexual trauma are encouraged to reclaim lost parts of themselves by practicing non-genital self-stimulation, a concept that initially may feel foreign. In other words, the focus of attention is on *sensuality*, not sexuality. Sometimes these classic sex therapy approaches are referred to as *sensate-focus exercises*. By titrating carefully chosen forms of touch and personal body exploration, a patient demonstrates a gentleness that respects and gradually reclaims the body. This kind of touch slowly acclimates patients to their sensual side and ultimately to the more anxiety-laden aspects of sexual expression. The entire time they are in charge of their bodies.

Limited massage therapy can introduce patients to safe touch, especially when the patient guides the initial activity. Methodically, they relinquish control of the massage sessions to the masseuse while staying focused in the moment. Movement therapies and dance can help victims become more sensual and comfortable with their bodies. Eventually sexual touch, in the form of masturbation, can become a way to resume sexual pleasure before allowing another person to intimately stimulate their bodies. What is learned along the way is that genital touch is but one form of sexual expression. Late in therapy, patients may want to rewrite their entire sexual *lovemap* in a way that is more personally meaningful to them, and no longer follow along lockstep in the ways they were socialized to accept without question.

Talking is vitally important during any sexual activity, especially following a traumatic event. The human mind is inclined to wander unchecked if a person simply lies silent and still during sexual activity. Invasive thoughts and emotions from the past can infiltrate the present. The mind automatically will go to a default state of commentary and judgment when a person's attention meanders away from the present moment. By applying sensate practices with a safe partner—verbally guiding, acknowledging, experiencing, and processing all forms of touch—the patient is better able to stay in the present. Hearing the voice of her current lover can also help to separate from the past.

After being abused, many persons go through a period of harsh moralizing, both about themselves and about their abuser. Religious injunctions can find their way into the bedroom turning what could have been a spontaneous and playful sexuality into a rule-laden encounter. When, however, abuse victims can grasp the concept of a *spiritual sexuality,* they are well on the way home to themselves and better able to meaningfully connect with a lover. It refers to the ability to rediscover what is beautiful, authentic, and sacred about yourself through a loving connection with another human being. Spiritual sex often accompanies a soul retrieval. By fostering a spiritual sexuality a person doesn't fear momentarily merging with someone else, even though past abusive influences suggest that could be dangerous. We all have a natural desire to intimately connect with another person to satisfy a very primal need for affiliation, especially when it is someone who honors and dignifies us, someone who reciprocates kind care, and finds meaning in lovemaking. Sex is not just about pleasure, recreation, release, demands, or power over someone. Nor is it about strict religious injunctions, the rights and wrongs of sex. Spiritual sex is the culmination of increasing intimacy brought about by sharing, revealing, affirming, risking, pleasing, and appreciating. It is rooted in both emotional and physical needs that are eagerly met by the lover, often during what is called *slow sex* (Daedone 2011). This is when a mindful and patient focus on the body's sensitivity shuts off distracting mental chatter, thereby allowing the natural expression of pleasure. No haste is involved. Touch and sexual pleasuring is enjoyed in the moment. It is not about rushing toward a grand explosion of simultaneous orgasms. I believe Walt Whitman was referring to spiritual sex when he wrote the following: "We are seas mingling, we are two of those cheerful waves rolling over each other."

Chaos and Rituals

When our world has been turned upside down by unpredictable events, chaos is felt. Routines are disrupted and everything seems unpredictable and people appear increasingly unreliable. That is why rituals are so very important in the recovery process. By their very definition, rituals are organized events that make and preserve order in times of uncertainty. Their orderliness, structure, predictability, sacred nature; their grounding, calming, and mobilizing qualities; the way they pull in community, and the way rituals reorient and transport us to new possibilities are but a few of the essential elements in the post-trauma change process. Rituals provide a secure road map out of chaos.

From the teachings of indigenous cultures, we know some of the basic elements for healing involve rituals that utilize earth, wind, water, and fire. The earth takes us back to our primordial, ever-present, and dependable mother. She drinks in our tears and transmutes them into new life. Many healing rituals can occur while standing or sitting barefoot on the land, receiving her recalibrating and healing electromagnetic energy (Ober 2010), a science of spirituality I was never taught at university.

The wind represents movement. Cares, offerings, and prayers can be offered to the wind and transported away. Smudging for cleansing and purification is an old ritual where the smoke of cedar or sweetgrass disperses in the wind, symbolically reminding us that all problems fade into the world around us with time. They are absorbed by the greater, life-sustaining universe. Water rituals can remind us of the need for change, flexibility, and flow. An old saying instructs: "We never stand in the same river twice because the river is never the same, nor are we." Standing in a stream releasing undesirable memories and hurts can create powerful lasting imagery. Water can symbolically wash away painful emotions and cleanse a once despoiled body.

Finally, fire is about transfiguration, a dramatic and sometimes sudden alteration in form. When a candle is lit and steadily drips fading into non-existence, when a flame is blown out, or as a list of grievances is burned and carried away by the wind, fire can symbolically represent the transient nature of problems. When fire rituals are incorporated into healing ceremonies, an important idea is planted in the patient's mind, that transformation is about to occur.

Chaos is about a person's life being stirred up, readied for change. I'm not saying traumatic disruption is fun, but I will contend that it is often necessary to dissolving the ego and discovering a truer self, one that doesn't wear so many faces, so many masks. To fulfill one's true life purpose it may be necessary to experience the driving force of chaos and fire. The role of the therapist is to be a wise anchor, steadying and helping the patient stay focused amid distractions. We must be unafraid to sit with the fire of tumultuous events and emotions, standing watch for insights, and helping the patient make sense of swirling events.

Yoga

Exercise and breath work are critical to slowing things down and becoming calm and centered. There are many forms of yoga that can help with this and 1,000 times as many instructors. What I would like to suggest is the exploration of time-tested yoga methods that have been adapted to contemporary life problems. *Trauma-sensitive yoga* (Emerson and Hopper 2011), when provided by a professionally trained instructor who is versed in sexual abuse recovery issues, can provide a remarkably effective way to step out of the past and re-inhabit the body. Survivors and thrivers reclaim their bodies through self-paced exercises that encourage choice, control, and attentive gentle care—all vital healing elements that were not present during their trauma. When someone is abused, the person's vital center is temporarily taken over by the perpetrator. Trauma-sensitive yoga helps individuals connect with that vital center, what psychotherapists call the *inner locus of control*. Rather than avoid or punish the body (as victims may feel compelled to do) because it gives rise to many confusing sensations and pleasures, yoga slowly reacquaints past victims with their bodies while helping them to expose, visit, and modulate certain somatic and emotional states (some of which can give rise to temporary displeasure) without any alarms going off. After all, this time around, victims should be in charge of their own well-being. While it may be an instinctive response to avoid unpleasant physical and emotional states linked to abuse, thoughtful and active engagement of the body and emotions is the best way out of historical abuse. It is too much to expect the passage of time, by itself, to heal all wounds.

Jamie's Recovery

At the age of 17, Jamie was a successful student in her rural Wyoming high school. She was an intelligent, attractive, vibrant, and vivacious young woman with an infectious joie de vivre that drew both peers and adults to her. Her computer science instructor and the school's highly regarded football coach, Mr. Johanson, offered Jamie individual mentoring and showered her with complimentary attention that filled a void created by an abusive natural father. Sensing her vulnerability, Mr. Johanson groomed her until Jamie would accept his fondling during private moments in her semiprivate computer module. Like so many victims caught in a situation they are totally unprepared for, Jamie froze with a nervous smile on her face, which her teacher chose to interpret as enjoyment. Then by surprise to everyone, Jamie's younger brother walked into the classroom one day and witnessed the teacher leaning over her while touching her breasts. Jamie's trance-like state was broken by the sound of her brother's raised voice.

A police and social service investigation followed, charges were levied, and the teacher retained one of the two most famous defense attorneys in Wyoming. He entered a "not guilty" plea and a jury trial was scheduled. Reality hit home for Jamie: This wasn't a special friendship, this was exploitation! Her teacher, on the other hand, was far from facing reality. His denial was complete. With help from his wife and his attorney, he positioned himself as the forebearing victim of a troubled student. Jamie's anger skyrocketed. Her hurt and betrayal were intense. When many of her fellow students sided with the coach, and members of the football team referred to Jamie as a slut, another layer of victimization was applied. But it didn't stop there. Parents of her classmates joined the controversy, the vast majority siding with the well-liked and handsome coach, generating still more stigmatization and powerlessness for Jamie to endure.

Ultimately the court ruled in favor of the defendant, and Jamie collapsed on the courthouse lawn sobbing. This time it was the legal system and the community that had abused her. There was no public recognition of her reality, no honest attribution of responsibility, no consequences applied to the perpetrator, and Jamie's abuser continued to work and reside in the same small town. The community was now fully convinced of the teacher's innocence and equally convinced of Jamie's devious and manipulative ways.

Conventional counseling began. I was her therapist. For Jamie, reviewing the chain of events was akin to ripping the scab off a never fully healed wound. She had counted so much on justice being delivered and the courtroom providing closure that anything less was heart-wrenching. Trying to put some distance between herself and the abuser, Jamie stopped referring to him in the formal school way as Mr. Johanson, and as Tim, the way he had asked Jamie to address him on a more personal level when they were alone. This wasn't a relationship of intimacy, she concluded, this was about exploitive intensity masquerading as intimacy. Again and again Jamie would say, "Just once I wish Johanson would own one small fraction of what he did to me, just once!" But it was not going to happen with all the social and legal maneuverings.

That is when the idea of a restorative-justice healing circle, using a surrogate abuser, was born. At first the idea seemed improbable, if not dangerous. The risks seemed huge, the capacity being there for still another disappointment, another letdown. Yet Jamie wanted to direct her own recovery and asked me to explore who, if anyone, might be available to help her in this way.

A former teacher was discovered who offered his help as a surrogate. He had once abused a female student, spent years in prison for his crime, and eventually returned to his community and was hired to offer technical support to sex abusers in a local penitentiary. The warden, penitentiary counselors, and local police all endorsed the man as being of exemplary character and as a good candidate to sit in a restorative-justice healing circle. His recovery program demanded reciprocity, giving back to the community and beyond, and he was eager to do something good.

After months of preparation, the day finally arrived when Jamie would have her chance to be heard in a controlled setting. It was her opportunity to voice her anger (in a dignified way) toward the surrogate stand-in. It was also a chance to get some answers to those, "Why me?" and "Why did you lie through your teeth?" questions. Jamie's cadre of well-prepared supporters was there to bear witness to the truth-telling, to hear any possible apologies, and to validate the proper attribution of responsibility. Sitting in a large circle with tissue boxes scattered about, the ceremony began with an explanation of the ground rules of respectful care: speaking only when the talking piece was in your hand, and allowing Jamie to guide the event for however long she desired. The circle was justice focused and victim driven.

The surrogate sex abuser's anxiety was evident to everyone. He rapidly tapped his fingers on the arms of his chair and nervously bounced his feet on the floor. He didn't have to be there experiencing all that angst, but nevertheless chose to take a day off from work, drive 300 miles to support these strangers, the victim, and her family. It certainly was not an easy thing to do, but there was no doubt it was the right thing to do for everyone involved.

Jamie started the healing circle with words of gratitude for all those who had spent time preparing for her day. She thanked the abuser for coming but respectfully warned, "I'm not going to hold back. I may never get an opportunity like this again." He responded with a nod and continued to twitch. She issued a thank-you to her stepfather for agreeing to leave his handgun at home, admonishing him for even having entertained the thought of potentially turning her healing opportunity into another tragedy. Jamie reminded him, "This is *my* day, Dad, and I'm glad you are here participating on *my* terms."

Three hours of inquiring, imploring, and crying ensued. Piles of tissue were accumulated on the floor. No one took a break, or likely even had the thought of doing so. It was riveting, immensely tense, sad, but oh so inspirational and healing. Jamie asked all her tough questions, some of them repeatedly, just to be sure she understood everything that was being said. The stand-in abuser answered with patience and a candor that was evident to everyone. He held nothing back, verbally and emotionally, and to Jamie's great surprise, he issued a heartfelt and detailed apology for each and every mistake made by the abuser, doing so with a tearful conviction as though he had committed the very acts himself. Jamie sobbed, and sobbed, and sobbed. It was what she needed to hear. None of it was her fault and it was all a horrible injustice!

The gathering closed when Jamie felt it was timely to do so. She asked if we would all stand, remain in circle, and join hands as one family, the abuser included. Drawing from her religious background, Jamie offered a prayer of thanksgiving. Then she dropped her hands to her side and bolted across the circle toward the abuser. Everyone's heart skipped a beat. She grabbed him, hugged him, and sobbed some more. Finally, a degree of closure!

In typical restorative-justice fashion the breaking of bread followed, with a feast. With so many sad emotions having been spent, laughter began to fill the room. Jamie's mother, a school administrator herself, turned to her husband and was overheard saying, "The world needs more people like him," referring to the sexual abuser. From seemingly out of nowhere this stranger had appeared, stepped up to the plate, and provided a corrective experience for everyone in the office. It was a time of relief, of hope, and of restored belief in human nature. Absolutely everyone in the room was touched for life by the amazing events of that day. A powerfully positive experience had just paved over the darkness of Jamie's trauma. Lasting bonds were formed. Most importantly, a smile graced Jamie's face; she was the recipient of a vast love like she had never experienced before, and some of it came from a complete stranger. Like the Phoenix rising out of the ashes of her abuse, Jamie arose as a new and stronger person, a woman committed to surmount each and every life test that would come her way thereafter. She became a woman with enough life wisdom to become a counselor just a few years later.

Certainly there were additional components to Jamie's recovery. She received guidance around the concept of romance addiction. When she married, Jamie was willing to explore her relationship control patterns and the projection of her own issues onto her husband. Shame themes were addressed using a schema therapy approach. Positive psychology assessment tools were used to discover Jamie's many character strengths, virtues, and core values. But through it all, Jamie believed that with each new revelation, with each new insight, an even brighter tomorrow loomed in front of her. As the first Noble Truth of Buddhism posits: "Life brings suffering. There is no escaping that." Yet Jamie would be quick to clarify that with each adversity she has faced, growth has arisen. Life's difficulties were, at first, perceived as annoying but eventually Jamie always ended up at the same conclusion, they are really challenges and opportunities. It all depends on how they are faced. Just as a stiff wind can be seen by one person as an impediment to moving forward, that same wind, from the perspective of a pilot, is what is needed to be uplifted in takeoff.

Hardwired for Growth

The human soul has a compass, an inner knowing of what is important, what is vital to our survival and our growth. I imagine it to be a spiritual DNA. It guides us through a death process, when after abuse we die to any false sense of self and reclaim our authentic essence. It provides innate compassionate impulses that connect us to each other and are difficult to extinguish. The testimony of sexual abuse thrivers reveals that one of their greatest struggles is to retain the natural desire to love, despite being contaminated along life's way by the distorting influence of hurtful people. Thrivers have also taught us that forming a singular identity around being the victim of abuse can be a hindrance to realizing a fully open and loving heart. Their most authentic identity is not just who they became after surmounting a trauma, but who they were in the first place and how they retained their most desirable qualities after repeated tests. Thrivers, who make it through the dark nights of the soul, are often the individuals who have learned how to self-soothe, who have risked practicing self-compassion, whose caring spirit has been amplified in healthy fellowship, who say their gratitudes daily, who can suspend their customary way of seeing things to find a better path, who are lovers of truth no matter how painful it may be, who empathically "listen" one another toward wholeness, and who give to others in a way the Dalai Lama has called "wise selfishness," a way of giving that feeds themselves too.

The wind of divine grace is always blowing.
You just need to spread your sail.

—Swami Vivekananda

FIVE

Vicarious Resilience

Our capacity to help others ... is greatest when we are willing,
able, and even determined to be helped ourselves.

—LAURA VAN DERNOOT LIPSKY IN *Trauma Stewardship*

Mental health professionals employed in the trauma field will most certainly be impacted by their work, both negatively and positively. Fully immersing ourselves in the pain of our patients can result in the development of similar symptoms whereby we mirror their experiences. As healers, our personalities can be destabilized from being in the company of other people's chronic pain. There are many terms that have been used to describe the hazards associated with trauma service: *vicarious traumatization, empathic strain, burnout, compassion fatigue, trauma-exposure response,* and *secondary trauma.* A high-speed life with an over-extended schedule can put us on course for burnout, and a slower pace can lead to eventual rust-out, but so can the need to be needed. Many therapists dive into the trauma field with an overly heroic, relentless, and addictive fervor. They are imperiled if they cannot recognize their over-giving and over-responsible nature and its origins. Driven to do good, their best essence is rapidly depleted. The result is to feel disillusioned and hopeless, perhaps a bit jaded and cynical as well. Once the therapist begins to spiral downward under the emotional weight of continuous comforting and countertransference, their patients' growth may become impeded and stall out.

As patients wear down from the chronic emotional strain of unresolved pain, the process takes its toll on the body. Stress chemicals, like cortisone and epinephrine, can keep the body hypervigilantly on high alert. Without working our trauma through, physical systems begin to break down. The immune system can be weakened, the adrenal glands become exhausted, and a cavalcade of inflammation-based disorders can unfold such as chronic fatigue syndrome, fibromyalgia, and arthritis. Therapists are not immune from the psychological contagion effect. Consequently, self-care will be vitally important if we are to be completely present and fully energized in support of our patients.

Burnout

Burnout refers to a distracted period in life when individuals disconnect from their own lives while remaining committed to the service of others. It is about chronic frustration and disappointment, wanting things to be different than they really are, and focusing on outcomes that never come to pass (Kissel Wegela 2009). Burnout can be viewed as a trauma for therapists. As with other events that are emotionally draining, it holds the potential to lead its victims into a more balanced life of meaning and purpose. The lessons that can be extracted from burnout are usually profound, life changing, and available for personal betterment. Recovery from burnout (or rust-out) entails the recognition of idealistic aspirations that healers bring to this work, which, while beautifully inspired, may have been somewhat unrealistic and consequently were not fulfilled. Burnout is a time of awakening when health-care professionals learn important truths about their inner selves. For those who seem to get the most out of serving trauma patients, they recognize that their role, while seemingly small, is incrementally important. It has to be focused on one person at a time, with whoever is in front of them at any given moment. The accumulated weight of previously treated patients has to be put aside for the person immediately before them. In *The Resilient Practitioner* Skovholt (2001, 184) quoted a mental health worker who said: "I have a sense of spirit. I have a sense of reverence. I have a sense of place in the universe even though I know it's just a speck; it's a place to participate. I believe there's benevolence in all that. I believe that warm, gentle breezes blow my way besides the cold, bitter winds."

Professional Maladjustment

Martin Luther King Jr. once spoke of the beauty of *maladjustment*. The term isn't normally thought of as being positive, but King challenged us to see it in his characteristically provocative way, arguing there must be a healthy degree of maladjustment in the face of unhealthy social forces. He wanted everyone to reflect on how they often sleep-walk lockstep with the masses, whether in the profession of psychology or in religious traditions, and self-protectively adjust and adapt to certain harmful and unquestioned traditions. A well-adjusted life, King suggested, is never complacent around maltreatment, no matter how dressed up its purveyors may be. In that vein, he suggested we may have to become firebrands and risk the criticism or even contempt of our colleagues when we question antiquated thinking that harms people. King believed there was hope for the world as long as enough maladjusted people were speaking out and opening eyes to mistaken ways of the judicial system, the law enforcement system, and so on. This should never be done in hubris, King cautioned, but with a humble dignity that comes from knowing you are aligned with justice.

Maldioma Somé (1994, 119), a Dagara shaman from West Africa, has written, "There are times when disobedience heals a very ailing part of the self. It relieves the human spirit's distress at being forced into narrow boundaries." When we challenge paradigms, raise temperatures, cast light on what we believe should be regarded as controversial, disturb public complacency, or just plain "brew trouble," personal attacks will never be far behind. All too commonly we will be labeled as firebrands, troublemakers, malcontents, idealists, or bleeding hearts, essentially people who have lost all common sense and the ability to practice discernment. For a compassionate therapist, this will likely hurt. Being alone on this course can be a harbinger of burnout. So by taking a stand and being active patient advocates, we must be shouldered by a group of wise and reasoned colleagues who are unafraid to tell us when we have veered too far off track. We have to be careful not to seek to humiliate or destroy those who would seek to humiliate or destroy our patients, or someone else (often a colleague) will seek to humiliate or even destroy us.

At some time in our careers we may have flirted with being more outspoken, more maladjusted. Just recall those times, especially in university days, while reading Thomas Szasz, Jeffrey Masson, Carl Jung, Peter Breggin, or R. D. Laing, whose words we found so refreshing.

They may have said things we wish we had the courage to imitate. Their way of expressing maladjustment often resulted in colleagues describing and even diagnosing them as disturbed. Each one has paid a price for not following marching orders, for not engaging in *group thinking*. Laing, as one example, found out that his intellectual challenges of the healing professions, his defiant personality, and a brash outspokenness resulted in a painful inner hurt and sensitivity that may have contributed to his eventual chemical dependency. As Adrian Laing (2006, 390) wrote of his father in *R. D. Laing, A Life,* "His real intention was to find a way to articulate his anger against mainstream psychiatric practices, which he always felt to be infinitely more crazy than the utterances and behavior of the so-called patient." Yet, his intentions were not always noble. His son wrote that perhaps Laing had burned out, that he had come to hate society for all its ills. Furthermore, in his growing isolationism, he came to view professional disagreements much like Freud did, as personal betrayals. Laing's shadow side, his blind spots, were projected onto fellow professionals, with patients being his almost exclusive source of ego nourishment coming in the form of adoration. Late in his life, Laing was challenged by the equivalent of a board of medicine; they accused him of being impaired and his fitness to practice was challenged. Laing was depressed and alone. He died shortly thereafter, important parts of his message left unheard.

If we monitor our pain the same way we advise our patients to do, one of the common fears of many psychotherapists is not so likely to occur—namely, "falling off the deep end." But it still may happen, and if it does and the truth be told, our patients will have handed us numerous templates loaded with tips on how to get back on our feet again. You see, we just are not always the rock stars we set ourselves out to be. Patients, often more than colleagues, tacitly give us permission (and often nudges) to be our most vulnerable and honest selves. They cooperate with our plan to love people for a living. Now where else do you get to do that? What gifts! Gifts to be unwrapped very mindfully.

So what are the lessons to be learned from this? First, a balanced life is necessary to enjoy, survive, and thrive in the mental health field, particularly working with trauma. This means I will strive to have the best and most up-to-date education available to help my patients, but I will always try to fit in a hike and a Cubs game. On any given day, positioning myself in the smoothest-running ticket line may be every bit as important as professionally positioning myself in the mental health business. Second, it is wise to develop honest, supportive, transparent, and safe relationships with open-minded colleagues. Being a maverick may be prudent at times, but it is not an identity I *must* develop and maintain. Third, sometimes it will be imperative to go against the grain in order to be aligned with our true selves. This can invigorate our moral energy and awaken positive vitality without coming across as (or being) self-righteous, acerbic, or alienating.

Despite the pessimism that can arise from living in a very violent and exploitive culture that produces a seemingly unending stream of victims, our own optimism and growth are spawned as a result of balanced, thoughtful, reverent, loving, and committed individual patient care. Done well, psychotherapy has attractive and infectious qualities. Seen this way, a brush with burnout can be regarded as a transitional learning time, a period when we rethink old patterns and develop new ones that will ultimately serve us and our patients better. During periods of burnout our soul is no longer whispering to us, it is shouting, "It is time for change!"

Trauma Stewardship

As trauma therapists have grown and become more mindful of their professional perils and potential enrichment, new terms have been coined to describe their positive responses. Van Dernoot Lipsky (2009) has introduced the idea of *trauma stewardship*. The concept refers to a daily practice that brings a quality of presence to psychotherapy, when suffering is transformed into meaningful growth and healing. As therapists are healed alongside their patients, this mutual resonance establishes a forward momentum that is mutually contagious, just as its counterpart, pain, can be. As healers we are challenged to model a healthy approach to life that can readily be witnessed and conveyed to our patients.

Compassion growth, compassion satisfaction, stress resistance, vicarious resilience are new terms that describe how therapists are touched in good ways while they serve trauma victims. When healers are exposed to patients that model astonishing courage, optimism, and resiliency in the face of unimaginable pain and suffering, often they too become inspired to re-examine their own lives and make needed changes. Working with highly motivated patients can satisfy a calling in many of us, one that finds expression and serves us well while we serve others. This often happens when we bear witness to and internalize the messages of inspirational beings. We become filled with awe, amazed by the strength summoned by deeply wounded individuals. Deep compassion, when matched with a balanced life of self-care, is a recipe for vicarious resilience.

Suffering is made up of, in large part, the thoughts and inner commentary occurring between us and the challenges we are faced with. Many philosophers have said that from suffering we *discover* life's meaning. With an avalanche of challenges some people, however, give up and surrender to depression. But an ever-awakening therapist recognizes that it is his/her duty to *invent* meaning in those moments. It was Thomas Ogden (1993) who encouraged the development of a "dialogical space" within ourselves, to be aware of our increasing developmental duty, year by year, to create healthy cognitive and emotional responses to life events that are born from observing the experiences of others. At any challenging time, for example, even if someone is handcuffed or jailed, the individual still retains the freedom to look at things from multiple perspectives. To exercise our mental muscles by holding a thriver's point of view is critical, especially if we are to expect the same from our patients. This level of commitment, this resolve, this fight, is the stuff of transcendent moments. It is characterized in the old Zen Buddhist quote, "Now that my barn has burned to the ground, I have a much better view of the moon."

One of the hazards of this profession is that many of us come to believe we are very special. This narcissistic belief is a logical reaction to being called upon, again and again, supposedly to save lives. A rescuer's mentality is usually supported by a sense of self-importance and perfectionism. In contrast, humility, good humor, and an ability to surrender, not taking ourselves too seriously, but still recognizing our patient covenant as sacrosanct, allows truth and growth to flourish while we inhabit the crucible of adversity. When a guilt mentality pushes us to do good, the driving force is inherently unhealthy. Guilt can only sustain us for so long before it burns us out. However, when love is expressed within professional parameters, everyone thrives. Like fear, guilt stymies forward movement. Fear of failure indicates therapy has become about us, not the patient; it undermines empathy and altruism. Love, because it is naturally other-directed, is a strengthening force. It is a caring human involvement during times of struggle, a concern that recognizes we have much in common with others and there is little that separates us.

Intentionality

As is the case with the patients we serve, for a satisfying life we too need to be engaged in lives of meaning and purpose. This requires some careful professional posturing. It can be emotionally draining to be in the trauma counseling field if our ego needs are the primary motivator. Ego wants us to be admired, to become famous, or to acquire wealth as a result of positioning ourselves in the trauma recovery field.

Abundance ministries are popular these days, even in religious communities, where pastors preach that people will be justly compensated with material rewards like flashy cars and extravagant homes for practicing good deeds. This is very different from the less complicated motive to understand and relieve suffering, which can bring personal joy and pay the bills too. While a dichotomous viewpoint isn't being stressed here, with one way of practice being better than another, it is important to be mindful of our intentions, motivation, our moral energy, and moral vision, so that the majority of the time we are guided by our best essence. For many therapists, being embedded in the philosophies of *mindfulness therapy* and *positive psychology* enables them to tap their own signature strengths and to practice out of their best selves. It is *good medicine.*

Equanimity

Equanimity is a target state of mind for our patients, but just as importantly it is a goal for every therapist. For much of my adult life I have sought equanimity. One problem was that I was unsure on how to define it. So how would I know when I found it? With that as a backdrop, let's try to understand this ancient principle.

Sometimes patients will master their own traumatic experience by acting it out toward us. Winnicott, back in the 1940s, taught us that there are situations when the most important thing a therapist can do for patients is to weather their anger and destructiveness. To tolerate emotional volatility can be healing for the patient, but potentially harmful for the therapist. Equanimity is the ability to maintain a clear and unshakable mind, especially during high-stress periods. It is a state of mind that allows us to remain intimately connected to the pain of our patients, silently processing their pain while, at the same time, being internally nonreactive. It is honing the ability to stand back and observe the big picture, but maintain at an even keel, staying fully in charge of how we respond to circumstances and stimuli. Equanimity is the ability to develop and maintain a buffer zone between our ardent feelings and our responses to them. It is the talent for tolerating stress but not being "hooked" by emotional content. We remain emotionally alive but as a Native American colleague once said, "We wear the world like a loose blanket" (Jones 1995, 152).

Mahatma Gandhi (Fischer 1962) referred to equanimity as a stable inner core that arises during times when we are surrounded by swirling action but, remaining unaffected by it, our destination still remains clear. From Gandhi's perspective therapists who display equanimity care deeply about their patients but whether faced with the bite of fire or ice, tumult or chaos, they remain steady, deeply contented, and on course. Realistically, as Hanson (2009, 117) wrote in *Buddha's Brain,* we are always reacting to patient content but, "Equanimity means not reacting to our reactions." In other words, we are fully aware of our emotions during sessions but have a circuit breaker system that keeps us from blowing a fuse. From a neuroscientist's perspective, our amygdala and basal ganglia, the fear and anxiety regions of the brain, are being monitored and controlled by the frontal lobe, the seat of insight and restraint.

Equanimity is the quality of mindfulness that allows us to let go of things over which we have no control. Not to be confused with indifference, equanimity is about being unperturbed by events knowing, in part, that they too will pass. It is also the byproduct of having made friends with ourselves, our own emotional condition. That peace is brought into the therapy room with us. In this manner we become a safe container, an exoskeleton of support for patients who are erupting with strong emotions.

We can develop equanimity by practicing *spacious awareness*. When I would sit atop a mountain on a Wyoming evening I could see my worries in proper perspective. I learned there is a boundless universe in front of us and our tiny thoughts and lives are simply bouncing around in endless space, untroubled because they are not on a collision course with anything, they just *are*. Space is needed for clarity and calm. We simply observe our thoughts and feelings coming and going, not giving too much importance to any of them in the grand scheme of things. We can be unafraid of emotions when we recognize they are illusory creations of our own mind. We can be unflinching in their presence because they do not control us, we create and control them. Comparing a strong emotion to a strong itch, we notice it but don't feel compelled to habitually scratch. Equanimity could also be seen as a parachute that opens during a free fall; it catches us and slows events down so that we can notice more. It takes years of practice to develop equanimity, but with this evolving skill of maintaining calm inner strength in our toolbox, burnout can be held in abeyance.

Slowing Things Down

The pace of modern culture is escalating. We are addicted to compulsive business. Mahatma Gandhi warned us about being swept up in the phenomenon many decades ago when he said, "There is more to life than increasing its speed." To keep pace with our over-scheduled agendas we multi-task whenever possible, while driving, while eating, even while conducting therapy sessions. A one-pointed mind is becoming a thing of the past. Being consistently distracted in this way is no longer relegated to those with an ADD diagnosis, more accurately it should be the diagnosis of our culture.

Multi-tasking is a sign of not being present with life; we are in multiple places with our minds. Strayer and Watson (2012) believe multi-tasking is a myth because it literally can't be done. It would be more accurate to describe the phenomenon as *cognitive distraction*. Despite most people's beliefs that they are the exception, that they can maintain multiple thoughts and activities efficiently, it just isn't supported by research. Out of 700 people surveyed by the authors, only 19 demonstrated an ability to divide their attention between people and/or tasks and still be equally attentive; many of them were airline pilots. The therapist who tries to be a multi-tasker outside the counseling office is likely to miss much of what a patient is saying when the door closes. Habits are hard to break. Additionally, while on the job, multi-taskers not only become less efficient and disappoint their patients, they also derive less satisfaction from their work while increasing their levels of stress.

It is important to remember that the present moment is not an enemy. We can sit in the present and survive quite well. Eckhart Tolle (2004, 84) in his typically succinct fashion wrote, "Stress is caused by being 'here' but wanting to be 'there.'" The popularity of his books is a clear indicator that he is addressing a truth: our culture believes it cannot live in the moment. We are apprehensive, worried, and afraid of the future while being forlorn, sad, and depressed about the past. So what are we to do, buck the entire cultural tide? Yes, if you want more calm and more satisfaction in your life, and if you want to be a better therapist.

Every time we are fully present with a patient we are in the moment. A series of moments that are not interrupted by the past and the future quiets the patient's mind and has a similar effect on the therapist. That is the beauty of psychotherapy. It offers us unlimited practice in being present and attentive so that we can live the life we are in. If we view therapy as an opportunity to empty our minds of everything except the person before us, we get a recess from our whirlwind culture. Being present in therapy allows us to unsubscribe from the past; in that way it becomes therapy for us too. People can survive virtually any moment. After all, we've done that our entire life so far. When we provide loving attentiveness during psychotherapy sessions two people are encouraged to grow in unison. Our patients heal and we heal. Now that's a survival plan!

More Self-Care Planning

If we monitor and sustain our own emotional well-being it is possible to stay strong and remain available to serve others. Beyond structural guidelines and theoretical models, there are many personal insights and practices that will enable us to practice "in a good way," as Native Americans would say. Similarly Buddhist psychology refers to *right livelihood*, when therapists practice their art in a way that is totally congruent with their best values, especially with regard to serving the Whole. By paying attention to our soul's compass, that inner calling, we help ourselves while helping others.

There are many lines of inquiry that can guide and promote the development of a healthy counseling practice. Consider the following questions about being very honest with ourselves, examining our humility, and lifting unnecessary responsibilities from our shoulders:

- Routinely consult your conscience about unrecognized agendas. Ask yourself, "Am I working in the trauma field for personal reasons of pride, financial prosperity, or to find answers to my traumas?"
- Regularly reflect on mistakes and failures, but without being unmerciful. Try to determine if self-criticism or perfectionism interferes with the spirit you desire to bring into therapeutic sessions. Ponder the reflection, "Do I engage in self-awareness or am I prone to self-indictment?"
- Do I see myself as the expert in the field, and if so, am I reluctant to seek collegiality and supervision?
- Do I tend to view my patients through the lenses of pathology and diagnoses, or by their positive personal traits?

- Do I relish the fact that patients are quite dependent upon me? Must I be at the center of their lives? Whose needs are being met by therapy?
- Am I willing to *unlearn* much of what I have been taught, especially those theories that no longer work well for patients? Can I be at ease in a mind of *unknowing,* where clarity isn't always attainable? Can I imagine growing as a therapist by letting go of old ideas, not just accumulating new ideas? How comfortable am I saying, "I don't know"?
- Can I be a part of therapy that is about collaborative co-exploration more than a problem-solving responsibility?
- To be an effective therapist is it essential that I overcome all my "sins and imperfections," or is it satisfactory to examine them consciously and non-judgmentally?

The following are postures that can promote a healthy mind and a healthy counseling practice:

- Practice gratitude, namely taking the time to routinely appreciate the blessings of balanced time in service and a life with many rewards.
- Recognize flow and my openness to personal change. Be alert to patterns of rigidity, when I feel things must go my way. Watch for the old disease process called "hardening of the categories," when I am inclined to pigeonhole people, myself included.
- Celebrate all facets of life. Allow awe, in all its shapes, forms, and colors, into our lives.
- Humbly note personal strengths, talents, and virtues.
- Suspend judgmental commentary (chatter of the mouth or the mind) when it is prudent to do so.
- Recognize the social boundaries that sustain me emotionally.
- Stay curious throughout life. Make sure this service to others fosters my creativity.
- Allow for play during and after "work," and even in sessions.

- Never be stagnant or fall into deep ruts. Grow and develop my craft, my art as a therapist.
- Be sufficiently organized, yet flexible enough, to maintain some control in my day.
- Be capable of giving myself permission to pull back from work when stress is accumulating.
- Be willing to take regular interior voyages to better meet and know myself (retreats and sabbaticals).
- Invent and re-invent meaning and purpose in my life.
- Be comfortable with my foibles. Be a neutral observer of myself and life.
- Stay awake to the fact that carrying kindness increases my vulnerability, and be okay with that.
- Realize that my happiness is not reliant on being continuously happy.
- Recognize how some habits can lead to sleepwalking or keeping me partially dissociative.
- Note and honor everyone's incompleteness.
- Recognize that as all people become softer on the inside, they become stronger on the outside.
- Develop the skill to be an increasingly solid container for change and uncertainty.

Indigenous wisdom guidelines for my practice:

- Be anchored in community, for personal healing and the group healing of patients.
- Rituals provide comfort, familiarity, grounding, and structure in a chaotic world, both for therapists and for patients.
- We are all woven together by a single thread. Seeing unity and connectedness between all people, victims and perpetrators alike, promotes healing.
- Be routinely grounded in nature. Literally spend increased time outdoors and plant our bare feet on Earth.
- Welcome spirits into the counseling practice, whether they

are departed ancestors, the spirit of a therapy dog, the lightness of a feather, or the spirit of burning sweetgrass.
- Where there is soul, there can be soul loss. Soul retrieval is my mission, with patients and with me.
- Recognize the elements of a healthy heroic journey or vision quest.
- Alertly move from the academic, linear, and logical, and allow room for the intuitive and mysterious.

And there are daily self-care activities that can sustain us as healers. Some of these are as follows:

- Debrief with colleagues every day, asking each other questions like: "What overwhelmed you? What gave you joy, satisfaction, hope, or sadness? What took your breath away? What precipitated any feelings of judgment, cynicism, or pessimism? What sexually aroused you, if anything, in today's sessions?"
- Maintain regular contact with influential friends and colleagues; this includes spouses, mentors, and friends. Each can serve a different function that we have identified and shared with them. Four types come to mind: One person may be an *inspiration* for us, much like an informed cheerleader, who notes and encourages the full flourishing of our best qualities. Another person may be our *confidant,* someone who provides a safe relationship in which we can be real, vulnerable, authentic, and fallible. Still another type of friend is our *challenger,* someone who is secure enough in the relationship to point out when we are off course, when we are distorting reality, or who can push us to the next level of health. Challengers know our values and our mission, and are not afraid to remind us when we have momentarily gotten off track. Finally, another supporter may be unavailable or even deceased. That someone may be a *heroic* mentor, like Joseph Campbell was for me. Staying in touch with Joe means watching one of his videos, listening to a CD lecture, or reading one of his books.

- Begin and end our days with some physical exercise, some of which is aerobic, while enjoying other relaxation activities. Examples include biking, running, hiking, walking meditation, kayaking, and yoga.
- Meditation time. This may mean sitting down each morning or evening to practice a formal discipline, like Transcendental Meditation when you repeat an assigned mantra and slide into trance. Other times meditation can be very informal; knitting may "zone you out." During the day it may be helpful to periodically regroup, sometimes with the help of some wacky humor. Finding some absurd Steven Wright, Jim Gaffigan, or Stephen Colbert routines online can be good medicine. For another person driving home from work can be a calming time while listening to a satisfying CD lecture series, rather than the depressing evening news. Meditation can be very casual, perhaps practicing deep breathing at each stoplight while on the way home. I like to listen to musical selections that help me punch out and adjust my mood. Louis Armstrong's and Eva Cassidy's versions of "What a Wonderful World," or Al Green's rendition of "A Change Is Gonna Come," can immediately redirect the emotional trajectory of my day. The key is to use some type of meditation to draw a demarcation line between patient time and our time, or between our stress-filled day in the office and the evening at home.
- Learn from smokers, even if addiction is involved. They regularly create space in their day, make time just for themselves by stepping away from work and going outdoors. For about 5 to 10 minutes practice deep breathing.
- Imagine if you initiated a morning meditation at your office, a ritual when each of you took turns reading the ancient Rumi poem below before starting the day:

The Guest House
This being human is a guest house.
Every morning a new arrival.
A joy, a depression, a meanness,

some momentary awareness comes
as an unexpected visitor.
Welcome and entertain them all!
Even if they are a crowd of sorrows,
who violently sweep your house
emptying it of its furniture,
still treat each guest honorably.
He may be cleaning you out for some new delight.
The dark thought, the shame, the malice,
meet them at the door laughing
and invite them in.
Be grateful for whoever comes.
because each has been sent
as a guide from beyond.

⤺

In this chapter I have tried to go beyond the usual ideas of preventing burnout while promoting resilience. Out of respect for you, the reader, I believe it isn't necessary to rehash the obvious advice like seeing fewer clients, scheduling more time between sessions, joining a bowling league, taking stock of your accomplishments, watching out for "should" statements, seeking more supervision, and so on. While I have included some variations on those themes, I really want to emphasize the formulation of new attitudes, new values, and new postures toward psychotherapy. Most importantly, to stay healthy and even to thrive in our profession requires an acute awareness of what goes on in our mind. With razor-sharp mental acuity, by thinking about our thinking, by practicing being in the moment, by being sure we are aware of who is allowed to rent space in our brain, and by avoiding the tendency to project our "craziness" on our patients, we are more likely to find our psychotherapy practices peaceful and satisfying.

Putting the ever-present desire for money aside, one of the best indicators of a healthy practice is when a person feels no desire to retire. Different from *workaholism,* which can be about escapism, perfectionism, procrastination, and resultant feeling of being drained, I am referring to a practice that leaves therapists feeling energized while in the service of others. When employment enhances someone's life purpose I don't hear the person say, "I can't wait to retire so I can do the things that I've wanted to do for years." I'm referring to the individuals who are in a state of grace, who actually enjoy working in the field of trauma recovery because it allows them to be in the flow, to express their spirit of self. Like the patients they treat, periodically they meet with failure and momentarily fall from grace. The experience shakes them up, and then lifts them up. As Sobonfu Somé, an African Dagara shaman, has said, "Failure is built into grace . . . Every successful person, everyone you respect, will tell you that they have mountains of failure behind them" (2003, 22). Failures are our teachers, our engines of wisdom. They center us and let us know when we are wandering, stagnant, or off path. As with our patients, it is after a serious struggle that we may need to be reminded that difficulties help us rise to a better place. Difficulties are totally connected with growth but our task is to separate them from disgrace. It is in community that this return to grace can occur.

No matter how high a bird flies, it has to come back to Earth.

—DAGARA TRIBAL PROVERB

SIX

Assessment and Interviewing

I'm a schizo-affective, obsessive compulsive, hyperactive para-
noid delusional depressive with bipolar tendencies superim-
posed on antisocial personality disorder... I've been given all
those diagnoses by one psychiatrist or another.

—PATIENT NAMED RALPH,
In the Realm of Hungry Ghosts BY GABOR MATÉ

Some oft-cited studies (e.g., ACEs) focus on the seemingly fateful correlations between the number and kinds of trauma people experience and the possible development of life-and-death problems that can arise later in life. This information is most helpful in determining when, where, and how mitigating social services are to be applied. Imagine tempering those common sobering (and often depressing) statistics by inspiring victims with the notion that sometimes fallen acorns can develop into sturdy oak trees. Trauma does not lock victims into a spiraling decline in their physical and emotional health. Nor must they settle for just enduring or surviving the sequelae; flourishing is certainly possible too. Health and thriving occur in the relationship between victims and the painful events they have undergone.

Abraham Lincoln may have started the positive psychology movement long ago, one could playfully argue, when in his inaugural address he referenced "the better angels of our nature." The phrase stuck in our American lexicon and concomitantly the concept of *good character* became one of the central organizing concepts of positive psychology. It stood in contrast with conventional psychology and the medical model that emphasized abnormality and the search for *character* or *personality disorders*. If we know what works for our patients, such as the growth experiences and admirable virtues that go beyond self-interest, we have one more method atop the ideology of illness with which we can foster mental health. "Looking on the bright side of negative events has been shown to be related to enhanced adjustment and experimental evidence demonstrates that instructing people to find the positives in traumatic life events causes health benefits as well" (Linely and Joseph 2004, 46).

Positive psychology treatment methods have been shown to relieve symptoms of depression best (55 percent of patients improved on all outcome measures), much better than conventional treatments (only 20 percent), and far better than drugs with treatment as usual (a mere 8 percent), according to Seligman (2011). The processes utilized involved building on patients' character strengths and personal virtues rather than simply calling attention to and remedying identified weaknesses, while assuming a biochemical basis for the depression. By enhancing the five elements of *well-being theory* (positive emotions, significant engagement, positive relationships, meaning, and accomplishment), a person is most likely to experience life satisfaction. When we, the therapists, foster optimism, resilience, and adaptive ways of relating to the world, we can expect patient resistance to diminish and their participation to endure over time. We will do a better job of assessing patients along these theoretical lines when we understand these concepts and have a template to follow.

Character Strengths

Getting people in touch with their signature *character strengths* and *core virtues* in an atmosphere of warmth, empathy, trust, genuineness, compassion, equality, respect, and good humor is one of the surest ways to advance patient growth and happiness. It is especially important to focus on matters of character when much of the trauma people experienced had to do with the diminution of their character. The personality insults may have been the result of social ostracism, bullying, domestic violence, or relentless character assassinations by disturbed parents, partners, or peers.

Abraham Maslow believed most people had a "Supreme Court" inside themselves that ruled on their phenomenological truths. As people developed their best-known traits, they could realize their potentialities, a process he termed *self-actualization*. Building on Maslow's compilation of traits found among self-actualized individuals, positive psychology has formulated a classification system for character strengths (Peterson and Seligman 2004). I have augmented that list with insights from other sources and use the compilation to guide patient assessments. The composite list of character strengths includes:

- *Wisdom from knowledge and experience.* Related features include creativity, originality, ingenuity, curiosity, openness to new experiences, open-mindedness, the ability to change one's mind, a flexible explanatory style, an inner locus of control, and a love for learning.
- *Courage.* Related features include bravery, willingness to risk under duress, perseverance, integrity under fire, vitality, vigor, and living one's life fully—like an adventure.
- *Humanity.* Related features include empathy, compassion, care, nurturance, love, reciprocity, emotional and social intelligence, attachment skills, generosity, and helpfulness.
- *Justice.* Related features include fairness, integrity, being a team player, showing leadership ability, and showing loyalty.
- *Temperance.* Related features include mercy, forgiveness, modesty, humility, self-soothing abilities, impulse control, judiciousness, circumspection, tact, and foresight.
- *Transcendence.* Related features include an appreciation of beauty and excellence, a sense of awe, humor and playfulness, realistic faith and optimism, a hopeful future orientation, and a set of spiritual beliefs that give meaning and purpose to a person's life.
- *Unity.* Getting off the "me plan" and onto the "we plan." Overcoming the delusion that we are individual and separate human entities. Selflessness.

For every strength and virtue, there is a language to finesse it. Learning how to structure an interview around these concepts is a skill many of us were not trained for at our university. It is important to be able to both spot and talk about external and internal strengths. External strengths may include community and family resources, while internal resources focus on individual strengths and virtues.

Assessing Strengths and Virtues

Very few positive psychology assessment measures were introduced to me as a part of my professional training even though some of them were already being developed in the 1950s and 1960s. My study time was spent understanding a few basic tests that measured signs of abnormal psychology, particularly the MMPI and the Millon, along with memorization of all the DSM personality and character disorders, ultimately labeling patients exclusively on their negative features. Of course I was also taught to never transparently reveal my findings to my patients, suggesting to me that either a) they were all too broken to hear the news, or b) perhaps there was something wrong with the existing methodology that didn't lend itself to helping them.

Today a search of psychological literature reveals scores of assessment tools that are now available to screen for the presence of all the aforementioned characters strengths and core virtues. Two of the best compilations can be found in *Character Strengths and Virtues* by Peterson and Seligman (2004) and *Positive Psychological Assessment* by Lopez and Snyder (2004) where you can find tools to assess forgiveness, religion and spirituality, quality of life, gratitude, attachment security, locus of control, problem-solving skills, self-esteem, hope, optimism, courage, humor, and more.

For the reader who may not be trained in the administration and interpretation of psychological tests, there are several very basic introductory books that present some fairly straightforward screeners and inventories that can help you isolate your patient's foundation of strengths. They may be used to gather data or to guide interviews or dialogues. Examples include books by Louis Janda PhD, *The Psychological Book of Personality Tests* (2000) and *The Psychological Book of Self Tests* (2006). Dr. Janda has gathered a wide variety of university-developed instruments that have been lifted from professional journals. Together these texts explore for a variety of positive traits: a sense of control over your fate, ability to regulate your moods, finding meaning in your life, the rationality of your world view, the capability for intimacy, empathy, the ways you love your partner, hardiness, friendliness, seeing the big picture, and your sensual potential.

Salvatore Didato (2003) authored *The Big Book of Personality Tests.* It provides very brief surveys that uncover strengths in the following areas: emotional wellness, creativity, mental flexibility, disaster responsiveness, imagination, ambition, thoughtfulness, control of your destiny, parental burnout, emotional intelligence, the capacity for empathy, and humorousness. The tests, while not particularly helpful for traditional diagnostic purposes, can be helpful in creating conversation around salient mental health issues.

The *Children's Strength Survey* can be administered by the parent of a child under 10 years of age, or older children can read and complete it on their own, receiving clarification as needed. Developed by Katherine Dahlsgaard, PhD, you can find it in the positive psychology text entitled *Authentic Happiness* (Seligman 2004). It measures traits such as: curiosity, ingenuity, love of learning, social intelligence, perseverance, valor, perspective, integrity, kindness, fairness, care for others, self-control, humility, hope, forgiveness, gratitude, zest, and more.

I also recommend returning to chapter 2 and utilizing the resiliency factors bulleted on pages 12–13. Using this information as a screening checklist with your next patient, both of you will likely uncover many resilient qualities that will augment the recovery process. This assessment exercise will help the patient move along the recovery continuum from survivor to thriver.

Treatment flows out of assessment. The task, for therapists and parents alike, is to shine a light on any talent or display of character strengths that serves the child well. We name them for the child to increase awareness of his or her capabilities. Each time a child becomes familiar with new talents while adjusting to new life challenges, it is like adding successive layers of armor that offer increasing protection as the child moves into adulthood.

Interviewing Principles and Exercises

There are two underlying tenets that guide a semi-structured interview: 1) I am here to understand your current pain and confusion, and 2) it is my intention to explore your life history, particularly those circumstances when you demonstrated some of your greatest flexibility and strength. More often than not, patients do not expect to be greeted and known in such caring and encouraging ways. With that kind of introductory style, we have just elevated their motivation and reduced some of their resistance to the healing process. They sense that we are not normal clinicians when the focus of assessment goes well beyond breakage to an archaeology of hope, the unearthing of abilities that may be momentarily quiescent, forgotten, or have atrophied from a lack of reflection or exercise. Their illness or malady will be discussed in relative versus absolute terms, pointing out what is realistically expected under such demanding life circumstances while highlighting their dynamic and organic nature.

With a healthy and realistic dialogue patients likely will come to the awareness that their present condition is a momentary, not permanent, alteration of their mental health. They have been temporarily derailed from their life path, having encountered a transitory impasse. This type of derailment will have qualities that are unique to them, but it is also something all of us go through at some point in our lives, in one fashion or another. We will discuss their resultant suffering with them, framing it as a normal and essential part of life, as "one of the engines of personal development" (Young-Eisendrath 1996). Interviews and discussions will scrupulously avoid promoting a "battlefield mentality" toward trauma and abuse. It will not obsess on external enemies, because that type of posturing only makes people more defensive and their problems seem more intractable. The best way to overcome evil is by making steady progress in the direction of that which is good. If there is to be any talk about warriorship, it will likely take the form of underscoring the fundamental bravery and courage exhibited by them, a developing fearlessness that is paired with gentleness. Additionally, there will be no talk about "divine saviors" or how therapists and gurus can supposedly show them how to totally circumvent pain. Similarly, therapists will politely discourage compliments about how *we* "saved their life." They are the ones who do the work.

While interviews are intended to gather meaningful information about people and their issues, it is also a time when, just by the nature of our inquiry, we inspire hope and slowly begin a process of exhortation. Not empty encouragement, but an active reflection of the patient's prior life successes that certainly should be recalled when amid a crisis. During the initial interviews we will also identify and mobilize both inner and exterior resources, from character strengths to supportive community services. Options are reviewed. During the first few interviews, patients will realize that they are not alone on this path; veterans of other conflicts may be asked to join their healing team.

Back in the 1960s Carl Rogers introduced us to the *organismic valuing process* (OVP). The OVP referred to an ability that is found within most people to know what is important to them and what is essential for a fulfilling life. This ability was not limited to academically trained psychologists who could, with X-ray vision and a few good tests, discern what is best for others. Instead, Rogers was insistent that patients had innate capacities to actualize and develop their potentialities. Therapists just needed to help patients peer into themselves and uncover their inner wisdom. One exercise that has helped me with this process has been to ask my patients to name three of their life heroes, living or dead, elucidating what it is about the luminaries they most admire. What I noticed is that the depictions of their role models usually describe the unrealized potentials that awaited development in them. Another exercise is to ask them to tell a heartwarming story, perhaps from childhood. In doing so, I frequently hear about the protagonist's personality traits and values that, again, represent underdeveloped or unawakened parts of the patient's character.

Borrowing further from Rogers, I encourage patients to be actively involved in structuring their sessions. When will we meet? How long should our sessions be: an hour, a day, or an extensive retreat? What do you think your homework should look like? Asking them what issues need to be addressed is always salient, but just as importantly I want to know what has worked for them in prior therapy encounters, how they have successfully overcome problems before now. I will likely inquire into their best aptitudes and how they believe they can be brought to the fore, tapped to address the job at hand. I may ask them about their dreams too. Not so much for the symbols and themes but more for any "call to action" that seems implied in them.

After decades of almost exclusively highlighting patient mistakes and defects, I learned of the *Good Lives model* (GLM) that re-ignited my enthusiasm to serve in the field of interpersonal violence. The GLM has been used with sexual perpetrators but is by no means limited to that patient group. This model posits that the pursuit of *primary human goods* (basic needs, experiences, and states of mind) orients a person toward the attainment of the goods. The quest for positive emotional states (versus seeking only to harm others) plays an important causal role in sex offending. Unfortunately, the goods are almost exclusively secured in maladaptive and hurtful ways. Nevertheless to engage abusive individuals in a dialogue about their harmful choices, therapists must have an interviewing style that coaxes out core needs and motivating factors, many of which may be quite normal.

Continuing with the example of sexual abusers, it can be posited that frequently they engage in sex acts not because they have a preference or orientation toward those sexual proclivities, but because some other basic need is being met during the exploitation. It is far more productive to interview abusers about the basic needs that are driving them and provide alternatives, than to interrogate in a way that obsesses on deviant sexual acts, a process that almost always heightens shame and generates resistance. Some abusers engage in harmful sex to meet affiliation, acceptance, power, and control needs, compensating for the alienation, rejection, stigmatization, and powerlessness they have known since the time of their childhood abuse.

Another approach to successful interviewing has been coined *Motivational Interviewing* (MI). It might better be described not so much as an interviewing protocol but as a *way of being* with patients. MI's foundational tenets are every bit as appropriate with abusive individuals as they are with victimized patients. MI is a non-judgmental democratic collaboration between therapist and patient. One of its goals is for the patient to experience the therapist as a supportive helper who listens more than tells. MI is based on positive, optimistic, and humanistic beliefs that sincerely convey acceptance of the core person sitting in front of us. In a safe therapeutic environment that promotes self-examination, power is routinely given to the patient to motivate a healthy change process. Repeatedly, as helpers we are responsible for revealing discrepancies and ineffective strategies that derail the patient from enjoying a satisfying life. Sometimes the discrepancies showcased are between a patient's good values and reasonable goals, and the choices and methods that have proven to be unproductive and hurtful. The interviewing focus moves away from a good or bad person paradigm to the neutral analysis of efficacy. In other words, patients are guided into asking two fundamental questions of themselves: 1) What have I been doing? and 2) Has it been helpful? For those of you who were trained in *reality therapy* interviewing skills, these questions will likely resonate with you.

Restorying

A skill I have learned from indigenous people of Peru is the importance of asking suffering individuals to create a narrative of their life and their painful experiences. Once that is complete, they are challenged to author a second story of what they intend to do with their suffering, explaining how it can be used to transform them in positive ways. Their imaginations open to new possibilities, but new neural pathways are opened as well, and in the process, the grip of victimhood is loosened.

Indigenous wisdom is resurfacing in the old/new field of *narrative psychiatry* that posits that psychiatry and psychology create pathologies out of natural human experiences. Victims of maltreatment and crime are frequently prompted to tell stories of their experiences, in part for ventilation and also out of a need to bring meaning to their lives. Unfortunately, patients can come to regard their stories as literal truths that cannot be changed. Helpfully, Lewis Mehl-Madrona (2010, 67–8) suggests that depression, pain, and fear are not static objects of conversation, not single photographs, but movies that can be edited. He has said, "If we reconstruct and retell our stories in the future, we can actually change and heal the past." From his point of view, "So-called psychiatric disorders are not disorders, but rather conversations that can be redirected, explored, and transformed."

Jonathan Haidt, in *The Happiness Hypothesis* (2006, 149), emphasized the importance of writing the story of trauma to assess what it had done to a person so far, but also to create a meaningful narrative, a larger narrative than the one our "inner lawyer" contrived. "No matter how well or poorly prepared you are when trouble strikes, at some point in the months afterwards, pull out a piece of paper and start writing." And when this is being done the therapist guides the patient to address two very relevant questions: 1) Why did this happen to me?, and 2) What good can be derived from it?

Hopefully it is evident just how incredibly important it is to have interviewing skills that do not deny patients' current understanding of their situation but can gently open their minds to a new narrative that builds on their best abilities to transform unpleasant circumstances. After trauma victims go through the law enforcement, judicial, and psychological systems, there is a real and present danger that their now "official" and widely documented victim story will become their identity, and a pathological one at that. The story starts to live in them. Consequently, ongoing meaning-making exercises can be introduced into carefully constructed patient interviews. Ideally our conversations with them can stimulate a new inner conversation. As the field of narrative psychiatry postulates, there are no bad people, only bad stories about people. Because the spirit of story is contagious, we encourage patients to spread a new one, even if at first it is just a therapeutic exercise in hope. The story of how they transformed their pain into a growth experience becomes much like a prayer, and thriving can be unleashed by having the right story for the right occasion. It may momentarily lighten their load and provide new direction.

To plant a seed of optimism therapists may recount some of what they have observed over the years in the confines of their offices. As regular witnesses to many human struggles we may have a treasure trove of stories to draw from. Anonymous tales of patient achievements can provide road maps for recovery, diminish feelings of alienation, develop commensurate hope in the therapist's skills, and serve to inspire and motivate. You can relay inspirational stories of challenges approached, problems surmounted, and instances when people walked away from tragedies stronger than before. The nice thing about stories is they are discreetly indirect and therefore don't invite much resistance. They allow patients to select tidbits, ideas, and solutions that resonate with them. From a discussion of the stories we can assess much about where their dreams reside and responsively develop approaches that will invite their buy-in. By learning to dream a new story, a creative act of manifestation is occurring. Stories, even when they are completely contrived, can contain the necessary primer and instructions for the healthy contextualization of a person's traumatic experiences.

While interviewing patients we must be careful to use language that implies a transient nature to problems—they come, they go. Our words are most helpful, and respectful too, when they do not imply breakage. As caregivers, we are honored by the opportunity to expand our patients' repertoires of ideas for how they can break a problem's grip on them, and we are fortunate to bear witness to their forward movement. Usually the problem's origins are portrayed as being largely external to them; the solution, however, comes from within. Maybe it comes from the toxic energy of thier abusers, the brainwashing that colored their worldviews, a legal system that is not bent toward justice, and so on. The responsibility for change, however, rests in large part with them and the application of their ever-expanding and increasingly effective storehouse of recovery skills.

Indigenous Guidance

Very often it is during near silence that a patient knows they are being heard, that their situation is being understood and properly assessed when we are fully present and when we are registering the full emotional impact. I can recall poignant interviews with Datoga tribesmen while sitting on the ground in their African huts preparing for a healing ceremony. Friends and family gathered around in a circle as I inquired what the pressing issue was. As an individual would describe the problem, point by point, everyone listened very intently. It was natural to affirm what was being heard with the whispered sound of a sudden inhalation. Each gasping "uhh" punctuated the remarks; much like an exclamation mark it was the equivalent of saying, "Oh my, that must have been difficult for you!", "I am so concerned about you!", or "I am with you, sister!" The simple vocalizations said so much while affirming the other person. The "uhh" expressed innocence, surprise, awe, and wonderment of the kind you would expect to come from a child, as if it was the first time they had ever heard something of that significance. The simple utterance showed great respect and support too, because it revealed how the person in pain was not alone with the problem, it was now being shared by others.

My visits to Bushman communities in Africa have taught me something about the assessment process too. When tribesmen prepare for a hunt, they often perform a ceremonial dance first. Mentally and emotionally they focus on entering into the mind and rhythms of the animal they are about to pursue. They dance in a way that imitates the animal's movements; they sing its song. Bushmen become in step with the animal. There is no rush to leave until full preparation of the mind has occurred. Similarly, making an effort to become in sync with our patients should involve a similar slow and thoughtful process. We can't just jump from one interview to the next without adequate reflection and preparatory time. It is vitally important to try to get into the psyches of our patients. We want to fall into the rhythm of their dances, enter into the emotions of their lives, and pulse with their hearts; then they can be understood and supported in the assessment and therapy process. That is when the hunt for insights and solutions will be most fruitful.

Psychological Weather Forecasting

While assessing patients, we are noting patterns in the clouds of trauma, gathering observations that tell us what storms may be brewing and where the sunshine may break through. We aren't just gathering information. Embedded in our interviews and conversations are ideas of what kinds of energy may be contained in the thunderclouds. A change in their psychological state should be as expected as a change in the weather. Both conditions are about the movement of energy happening in and around them.

Have you ever noticed how people rush to the aid of others after a calamitous storm? Storms often bring out the best in people. Similarly, after an interpersonal traumatic event, like sexual abuse, it is our instinct to rush to the aid of the person who is suffering, some being faster than others in doing so. The Dalai Lama has long taught us that the byproduct of such events is the development of a deeper compassion for our fellow humans. He suggests that periodic personal and national tragedies open our hearts to a greater love almost as if we need to be shaken up a bit to get back in the groove of loving each other.

A tornado or a hurricane can fill us with awe. Fear-inspired awe, of the kind that psychological trauma bequeaths us, throws us out of our normal comfort zones and can open us to new possibilities. Bad weather conditions, environmentally or socially, can catapult us out of old routines and into an eye-opening, new existence. They remind us of our powerlessness and of life's uncertainty. Like a rainstorm washes Mother Earth, the tears of our grief can serve to cleanse us of old ways and thrust us into growth. Storms balance energy after the collision of two opposing forces. Seen this way, it's all good weather (Moss and Corbin 2008).

Depression, anxiety, and addiction reflect a change in the mind's weather, when cross-currents and uplifting currents momentarily catch our attention. They may have their origins in biochemical, neurological, psychological, or spiritual forces that occur in and around us, but are not us. They are not to be diagnosed as a part of a person's identity or character, but we must know something about how to assess the many factors that energize storms of the mind. There are many texts that can help therapists expand the assessment process beyond psychological abnormalities. I have arranged some therapist-friendly books by topic in a resources section on page 117.

This chapter has expanded the methods of assessment that can be used in determining the sequelae as well as the strengths that trauma victims bring to counseling. In the next chapter, we will look at treatment from a soul-based perspective, emphasizing a posture that has sacred dimensions.

> *The poignant truth about human suffering is that all our neurotic, self-destructive patterns are twisted forms of basic goodness, which lies hidden within them.*

—JOHN WELWOOD in *Toward a Psychology of Awakening*

It is indeed astonishing to realize that students learn about psychopathology without ever being taught normal psychology.

—Antonio Damasio in *Descartes' Error: Emotion, Reason, and the Human Brain*

SEVEN

Soulful Counseling

Soul does not abolish the difficulty of our lives, but brings music
to our pains — its gift is to make us less perfect and more whole.

—The Light Inside the Dark by JOHN TARRANT

"**M**y son Scott killed himself last night," wrote psychologist Paul Pearsall in the last chapter of his book *Awe.* (2007). In previous chapters, Pearsall, a positive psychologist, noted that the emotion of awe is experienced when we have an open-minded, intense, un-edited engagement with the world around us. Awe can be invigorating. Awe isn't so much about feeling euphoric; it is about feeling life deeply, the joys, the sorrows, and the wonder. Awe also has a dark side and is sometimes fed by negativity and adversity. None of us get our way in life, but the difficult "way" is what feeds awe. In fact, when depression becomes consuming in our life, it is a sign we are experiencing reality more fully. Life very frequently is not fun, it may in fact be traumatic, but we are here on this Earth to feel the experiences of life and death deep in our bones. Pearsall believes that some of our greatest strengths arise in the grip of trauma. It is paradoxical that very painful life experiences commonly give birth to human strengths and are often the prerequisite to experiencing awe.

After the painful loss of his son, Pearsall decided nothing needed to be changed in his book. His mental map for life remained the same, not naïvely optimistic, but very realistic. He isn't held hostage by an unending pursuit of happiness. Strange sounding, perhaps, for some who think of positive psychology as being about smiley faces. Nevertheless, Pearsall's grief over his son's death was counterbalanced by some traditional Hawaiian humor that worked for him at his son's funeral. In his search for meaning that day, one of the Hawaiians in attendance said, "The only difference between an Hawaiian wedding and an Hawaiian funeral is that there is one less dancer."

Pearsall remains inquisitive and keeps on dancing. He still wants to know more about the dance of life, why we descend into pain so often, and why pain seems to be so interested in us.

Point of Entry

Traditional Dagara culture in northwestern Africa believes some individuals' life missions in the world of healing are predestined; they are even known before birth. A shaman may tell a pregnant mother what the newborn's life purpose will be and as the child matures into adulthood, a deep community commitment supports and nurtures the individual's path into his or her own developing, true nature.

Many therapists enter the business of healing as a way of positioning themselves in relationship to their traumatic past. Being a psychotherapist can be a way of saying, "I am passed all of that. I am now a healer." Sometimes wounded persons with a religious orientation will seek religious ministries as a way to be "ordained out of their shame."

Readying oneself for a soul-filled practice requires complete awareness of all that drives us. A new identity? A good income? A way to be affirmed as worthwhile? A way to find personal answers for our pain? A desire to serve? A natural expression of compassion? Becoming a healthy and effective therapist requires that we first discover self-compassion and learn self-care before we try to guide the healing of another person.

The Rewards and Hazards of Service

The *call to service* can offer much to relieve suffering and enrich other people's lives, but personal rewards are certainly not incidental. Many people in counseling and healing fields recognize a sense of personal urgency that drives them, matched with an idealism never lost after the university years, and an undying search for the reasons for human suffering. There are many exemplars who, at one time early in our lives, may have struck a satisfying yet restless tone that still resonates deep within us many years later. In addition to the many persons I have cited so far, I have taken additional inspiration from numerous other people over the years: the founder of my publisher, Safer Society Press, the late Fay Honey Knopp, who was a Quaker and an undying optimist in the sex abuse treatment movement; child psychiatrist Robert Coles; and social activist and pacifist Dorothy Day. Day likened being summoned to serve others as a "call inward," a call to oneself. We become watchmen of the night and, and as Coles (1993, 284) also wrote, "The darkness that defines the moment of light in us, the darkness that challenges us to shine for one another before, soon enough, we join it." If we aren't vigilant, as I cautioned readers earlier, serving can pull us down perilously close to futility, depression, and, potentially, burnout. This is not only a hazard of trauma work but it is also a hazard of a driving idealism.

When burnout happens a paralysis of word and action takes hold. Dr. Martin Luther King Jr. once described burnout as a "surrender." He cautioned that it is when we give so much, too much, that emotional exhaustion closes in; we end up surrendering to the worst side of ourselves and then display our shadow to those we are charged to serve. For our own sake, as well as the health of our patients, we must anticipate the perils of caring, one of which is that we will fail often. That is an expected part of the journey for some of the best and the finest among us. During our wise moments, however, we will take note of what was extracted from our setbacks. The hardships usually serve to hone our counseling and personal survival skills, their benefits being postponed for another day.

The Courage to Care

Some of the bravest people I have ever met were not gladiators in a sports arena. They weren't uniformed guardians on the streets or heroic soldiers. The truly courageous people have routinely sat across from me in the counseling room, grappling with foes that were not met on foreign soil or back alleys, but were confronted in their own homes, schools, and churches. Intimate betrayals are sometimes the hardest to overcome because the defining line between "good guys" and "bad guys" is often quite nebulous. Countless times I have been awestruck by the courage patients have displayed as they chose to approach their traumas and fears. But the flattery bestowed on myself as their selected therapist reminded me of the responsibility I had: to rise to my best level of professionalism while expressing the most awake form of altruistic love. I have been blessed with the honor of being a participant and a spectator in their struggles. It has illumined me to the best qualities of life that arise under the most trying circumstances.

In therapy we have the opportunity to climb alongside our patients to new vantage points, often sacred heights. Neither of us may feel comfort or security at first, but commonly we arrive together at a mutual destination of resolution. For this to happen we must offer the greatest usefulness, the most honest communication, the most exemplary faithfulness, fierce truths, the heartiest exhortation, and the deepest union of mind that brave women and men are capable of experiencing. And what else happens to us along the way? If we are asleep to much of what is happening, we may resign and move on. If we are wide awake to the gift of it all and take good care of ourselves, we will mature to new levels. As Cohen (2000, 158) revealed, "The only way I ever found to deal with my own suffering is to attend to the suffering of other people." This reverent communion of sorrow and care is like an orchestra or a dance. We become instruments that produce a new sound and new movement. Therapy can transfigure people when spiritual forces are invoked.

Many truly soulful counselors will tell you they were personally motivated by the courage of their patients. Having witnessed their monumental gains, patients many times nudge us forward in ways our own paid therapists could never evoke in us. They often teach us more than some of our best mentors and greatest professors ever did. And secretly, we often feel closer (while denying it publicly) to patients than some of our most intimate friends. That is all a part of the "seduction" and the reward of doing this work; we discuss some of the most vulnerable, personal, deeply private, and sacred aspects of the human condition in a well-controlled environment. We tap into our ability to offer highly focused attention to patients in a world that is otherwise fraught with multi-tasking and constant technological distractions. We offer them our riveted concern along with a full effort to understand and support them. No wonder we feel such satisfying exhaustion at times, feeling strongly attached to their journeys, being invigorated by them, and even flattered at times by their words of gratitude.

Renowned psychotherapist Jeffrey Kottler (1995, 147) wrote, "Clients give us the benefit of the doubt when they can feel our caring." At the same time psychiatrists, attorneys, or supervisors may not be nearly as charitable when they cryptically question us for coming to the defense of a patient. We are inclined to see the best in our patients but often set the bar somewhat higher for colleagues, friends, and ourselves. Providing therapy can bring out the best in us but we customarily return to our "loved ones" at the end of the day wanting to resume somewhat sloppier relationships, ones that don't receive the same level of effort. We may begin to doubt ourselves at that point, when we can recall how, during the majority of the day, we were able to access compassionate talents and abilities that now seem difficult to resurrect.

Throughout this book I have written about the many ways individuals can tap benefits from pain. Over his years of practice, Kottler (1995, 66–67) discovered that his own pain was his greatest resource. "It wasn't my knowledge or skills alone that made a difference; it was the stark clarity with which I could feel the pain of others and connect it to my core issues."

Automatic Pilot

Western psychology focuses heavily on training individuals all the techniques and guidelines that go into curing many unsatisfying mental states, what are usually labeled as *disorders*. Once we have graduated from university training and an internship has been completed, for the most part it feels like we have learned the craft. All the steps and protocols are etched into our memory; we are now "good to go," ready to heal. We wake up in the morning, work out, shower, eat, down a caffeinated propellant, and head to the office to do what is called *therapy*. Much of this important work is done on automatic pilot, often for decades. It seems as though there is a baseline automatic-pilot state that we have permission to operate from. Little thought may go into becoming *soul-ready* for the daily ministry that lies before us. We simply dive in and advise a series of abused patients, often one right behind the other for 8 to 10 hours, telling them how specific behavioral measures or pills will improve their lives. When the clock says we are done (and they too are presumably finished at exactly that time) we jump back into the car and head home. If we commit to staying wide awake in the healing process, we can't help but discover there are other ways of "doing business"—the ways of the patients.

Electing to periodically step outside the confines of our training and do a little exploring, a "field of knowing" can open to us. I have found that more often than not it is my patients who take me to this place as a result of their unabashedly unique ways of circumnavigating the world. I have become increasingly willing to acknowledge that my patients' "illogical" knowing, experiencing, and listening (even to silent and invisible things) have led them to profound therapeutic breakthroughs. Sometimes they talk about an "inner voice" and being "moved by spirit." I could easily find descriptions of similar phenomenon in the DSM-5 and, by nature of my professional training, be inclined to pathologize nearly all of it. By contrast, I could also go to an Indian reservation and discuss this seemingly mysterious process with an elder who might tell me that I am in the company of an uncommonly wise person, someone who quite likely is being broken open by the spirit of pain. I would be advised to allocate lots of time to the process, to take my wristwatch off, and settle in for an enlightening ride.

When therapeutic rituals (counseling techniques and protocols) are generically scripted, devoid of spirit, and are not led by the heart, there is a risk for emotional depletion. Additionally, when therapists feel responsible for their patients' happiness, it can be a large burden to bear. Taking a less directive, less technical, but more mindful and sacred demeanor into the counseling space allows both the patient and therapist to go on a gentler transformational ride. This entails some movement from the head to the heart, from strictly thinking to feeling and intuiting. In a reverent relationship characterized by a healthy balance of power, both parties are likely to experience parallel growth. Such is the value of a caring connection; first between two people, then in families, on to communities, nature, the world, and even beyond.

Formulaic approaches are potentially constrictive, unimaginative, and mechanical. They may not be very energy-filled, for either the patient or the clinician. This can result in a tired brain but not the rewarding exhaustion that comes with deep soul work (Mason-Boring, 2012). When two or more souls are driven by heart wisdom to move someone forward it often feels like a good physical workout has just been completed. People feel tired but tend to wear a smile on their sweaty faces. This is but one of the opportunities that comes from doing trauma work in the fashion I have been describing, when, as Native Americans say, we "walk together."

Ego and the Letters Behind Our Names

In my visits with dozens of indigenous societies around the world, I don't recall one shaman asking me to address him with that title. In fact, quite the opposite was usually true. The genuine shaman rarely tried to distinguish his status as being different or better than someone else. He or she was always humble. If an indigenous healer were to introduce himself as a shaman, it would almost be a certainty that he was not one. And rarely will you find letters behind their names—no *E.I.E.I.O.s* to puff them up.

Canadian physician Gabor Maté has commented on how unimportant it is to our patients to be guided in life by a healer who is approved and credentialed by his industry. What they really desire, he contends, is a genuine presence, someone to co-exist with them, someone sincerely committed to their well-being, a human being who relates to them as a person with honest feelings, hopes, and aspirations. Gabor Maté (2010, 25) has written, "When my addict patients look at me, they are seeking the real me. Like children, they are unimpressed by titles, achievements, worldly credentials. Their concerns are too immediate, too urgent." Working with Vancouver's heroin addicts, Maté feels like a mirror is being held up to himself as another human being, and to our collective society as well, so that we can better know ourselves. He said, "The fear, pain, and longing we see are our own fear, pain, and longing. Ours, too, are the beauty and compassion we witness here, the courage and the sheer determination to surmount suffering." Truth be told, our patients reveal us and inspire us. The primary difference is they write the checks.

Native American psychiatrist Lewis Mehl-Madrona (2007, 8) warned, "We doctors have an especially rich investment in wanting to be the main character in a medical-hero tale." That phenomenon isn't limited to just one of the healing professions, it runs across the board. Most of the healing arts are really healing mysteries. More often than we are willing to admit, patient growth seems to come out of nowhere but we proudly explain it in the context of what happened in some 50-minute sessions. We are positioned by our individual industries to be seen as experts who know more about our patients and their mental health than they do. Our professions claim to have the ability to heal people from a position outside of them.

With the help of humanistic psychology approaches, the healing professions are becoming more humble, increasingly open to standing with equal footing on the healing ground, and willing to respect the patients' personal knowledge of their problems as well as proposed solutions. In the ancient history of healing, Aristotle referred to *entelechy*, a vital force found in all people that moves them in the direction of self-fulfillment. Native American healers often have called these forces *spirit helpers*. Shamans know that the inner workings of each individual—his or her beliefs, worldview, and personal response to healing rituals—determine a positive outcome more often than the intervention itself. We now know that psychological and medical techniques don't have to be linear, logical, and "correct" to work.

Ancient indigenous societies rarely made distinctions between private and public worlds. And one of the beautiful things that can happen in today's soul-filled therapy is to witness how patients teach healers how to drop all the pretense, the show and bluster, and get down to what it is like to be another vulnerable human being living in a complex world. They usually don't come into the office trying to outdo us (although some impaired professionals have challenged me that way), they are just ready to show up and *be* and *be with*. To *be* is to step away from hierarchies and labels. It is a way of safely exploring one's inner light, the best essence flickering inside each and every one of us. It is about standing for something and being supported in the process. It is about not being involuntarily swayed by the rigid, the ridiculous, or the profane. It is about self-affirmation, a way of talking to ourselves that clears off the tarnish and toxicity of abusers and emotional vampires. It is about accepting darkness, doubt, uncertainty, mystery, and the dissolution of self in search of unity. We can't get fully out of the soul's crucible, nor should we, but we can always go further in. All of this happens best between two well-intentioned and wide-awake people in the therapeutic hour, or better yet, the therapeutic afternoon.

You may recall that the word *therapy* is derived from the Greek word that means "servant." Being with someone, fully, is to serve that person. It is not a portent of burnout if, however, we also are there to observe our own transformation in relationship with the other and are willing to grow at the same time. If we expect our patients to risk in the direction of growth, we must be prepared to do the same. Clark Moustakas (1995, 153–54) wrote, "I believe that life is impoverished when we dare not venture where we have not been before, when we are taught to fear moving toward the undisclosed, when we remain always safely in the light." Vulnerability is a fact of vitality. Each time we risk vulnerability we are a pilgrim again.

Unity

As healers we may inwardly shudder at the thought of how much we resemble our fellow humans, especially our patients. When unaware of this, we run the risk of separating ourselves from them by using objectifying labels, distancing ourselves from them, or ostracizing them because we fear just how much they resemble us, our past, or what we might become. In their dark mirror our own features and our potential can often be reflected. In response, we can run like hell or pause, ponder, and give thanks for the humbling lesson in unity.

Compassionate therapeutic care must originate from, and pass through, the caregiver first. I have noted how generally the most

beneficial and rewarding healing practices are the most spiritual practices, not necessarily religious, but spiritual. Psychological work can
be about finding ourselves, discovering the meaning of pain, creating
purposeful lives, and rebuilding self-esteem. This could also be called
soul work, that process of going inward and discovering an unfiltered
world of personal meaning. Just as important as it is to find ourselves,
it is wise to know how and when to let go of our individual identities, to *die unto ego,* as Buddhists call it. Ultimately the goal of therapy
(and of life itself), for both the patient and the caregiver, is to rejoin the
family of man—a return to the original state of unity. This requires a
spiritual immersion, finding the ways in which we purposefully belong
to the Greater World, one that is no longer made up of dichotomous
categories like perpetrators and victims. Divisions fall away as we do
the very hard work of getting to know the pain of oppressors, every bit
as much as we try to understand the pain of the oppressed. Their paths
are usually not very dissimilar, as all creatures are a part of the greater
Whole, woven together by a single thread of the past and present.

In therapy, this posture often involves applying the paradoxical
practice of *tonglen meditation,* when individuals sitting across from
an empty chair (representing the perpetrator of harm) breathe in the
abuser's imagined pain and suffering while, at the same time, releasing
their own suffering, which may be fueled by clinging to thoughts of
vengeance and separation. With each outbreath the meditator extends
a blanket of pure white love in the direction of the chair, offering care
even to those individuals who aren't liked, realizing that by compassionately connecting with them they too become the recipients of a
peaceful and healed heart. It is when we stay connected to our larger
being that suffering is diminished. So it shouldn't be too strange to
wrap our minds around the idea that abusers, including sex offend-
ers, offer ways for us to heal too. There is much to enrich us while in
the company of *all* our healing patients. Compassionately sitting with
the pain of a patients' abuse histories and witnessing the courage they
exhibit in the dedicated work to thrive, we also awaken to personal
healing.

When patients let go of the need to "fix" what ails them, and when
therapists no longer see themselves as "fixers," we have entered into a

new and more productive healing paradigm. As long as people demand that life must be different than it is, or better than it is, they remain locked in a battle that can't be won. Internal peace is that ability to sit with *what is*. It doesn't mean we shouldn't strive to make the world more peaceful, but rather to learn how to deal with it as it comes to us on any given day. As healers teach that to patients, they become what they teach. This posture of moving toward pain and flowing with pain, allows both individuals to go home smiling at the end of the day.

It has been said that if you are not enjoying therapy, you are probably doing it wrong. Investing in growth ought to be joyous. Watching patients make progress should be empathically satisfying. Finding the good in others just might help us see the good in ourselves. Encouraging patients to be more flexible, we often expand our own flexibility. As we help them, an internal dialogue goes on inside of us. When we find ourselves being increasingly more effective in the role of healer, it follows that we too will be healed in that purposeful existence. All of this comes with the openness to being swayed by ancient wisdom traditions, being "medicined" by the old ways, and allowing them to guide us along a slightly more spiritual path while still paying heed to contemporary, academic best practices (Blanchard 2011).

Now take this part sitting down. Could it be that the most influential factor in patient change is not the most recent, trendy, or innovative technique? Could it be that it is not about our laudable best practices, or research-based modalities? Could it be that it isn't even about the *use of self*, or the therapist's *personhood* that matters most? Maybe it is *the patients* who are responsible for most of their growth, especially as they unfold into their natural essence in our safe and compassionate setting, even amid our sometimes mechanical protocols and techniques. Maybe resurrecting *best essence* is as influential as following *best practice*. Long ago, psychiatrists Jerome and Julia Frank (1961, 167) posited the following, "The personal qualities and attitudes that patients bring to psychotherapy seem to have a greater effect on their response to therapy than does the technique their therapist uses." I believe their insight is as on the mark today as it was over 50 years ago. Consequently, we must have the willingness and the skills to maximize the gifts patients bring to our offices.

Ziji

From my exploration of ancient wisdom traditions, I have come across the word *ziji*. I interpret it to mean the brilliant confidence that comes from being anchored in our own peace, a peace that arises from no longer trying to prove ourselves to anyone—patients, colleagues, or even ourselves. We have moved beyond interpersonal deception. *Ziji* is a peace the results from being synchronized with the rhythms of the world. This level of contentment is tacitly conveyed in the quiet of a therapeutic session and is absorbed by our patients. It can resemble mercy, or as Sayong Mipham has written (2005, 82), "…having enough friendliness with our own mind to see someone else's predicament." It displays an element of tenderness that simultaneously develops when our personal fears diminish. It touches on aspects of our patients that are positive while, at the same time, our gently worn confidence provides a solid container for their sadness. Soon they realize that their happiness does not depend on being continuously happy.

Ziji can also be experienced as a self-assuredness whose recipe includes part courage, humility, warmth, and the conspicuous absence of desperation. It is evident when we are able to harmonize with uncertainty and the unknown. As we continue to *be* in peace, patient growth will be a natural byproduct of sitting with our *ziji* presence. This "therapy" is not about a technique or a protocol, but about a presence that is completely awake and fully human. Additionally, it is about an integrity that is born in deep connection with the patient, a way of carrying personal anguish, vulnerability, and incompleteness before others that does not deny the many obvious contradictions of the human condition.

Additional Lessons from Healing

Contrast for a moment, your last daylong business meeting with a group of professional psychologists or psychotherapists. Was there any posturing, competition, one-upsmanship, condescension, or inattentiveness by colleagues who were using their smartphones or talking over each other? Then reflect for a moment on your last few therapy sessions. In which setting did you observe the kindest behavior? If it was in therapy, as I suspect it was, you are likely doing something right. Rarely, when we are in the company of colleagues, do we risk dropping our guard and being vulnerable. Rarely do we listen so attentively and show such deep respect as we do in therapy sessions. Our patients help us practice being our best and, as a tandem, we tend to bring out the best in each other. This is often the contrast many of us have experienced dealing with the politics of professional organizations and licensing boards.

Much of what society has learned about the human experience has come not from the heights of accomplishment or the places of plea-sure or fantasy, but from the depths of despair, what I have frequently referred to as the "dark nights of the soul." Thomas Moore (2002), an expert on the subject, wrote, "Transcendence arrives when you embrace the life that is given." You are satisfied with what is. As much as we tell our patients that healing formula, I for one have frequently found it difficult to live by that credo, especially when it felt like I was in a free fall. Yet, in hindsight, it was absolutely true.

Another lesson I have learned is that the most effective therapeu-tic alliances are horizontal rather than vertical. When I have given up being the expert of someone else's experience, growth (for both of us) was more likely to take place. This egalitarian insight came quite early in my career, probably because my own self-esteem was rather tenu-ous. Rather than trying to be a magician or a superstar in my patients' eyes, or those of my colleagues, I was more inclined to conclude that my patients knew more about themselves than I could ever discern. Modestly, I just offered to help out wherever I could. Eventually, I picked up the "art," which was largely about being present. Being an effective healer had more to do with being real than being brilliant, although information (which I confused with wisdom) was always somewhat comforting to me.

Most of the problems patients risk disclosing in our presence, and most of the traumas we grapple with as therapists, aren't described well by the language of the DSM-5. I have come to prefer the conceptual-ization of human problems used by psychiatrist Stanislav Grof, seeing them as *spiritual emergencies*. Crisis is a transformative breakthrough about to happen or already in the process of unfolding. Spiritual emergencies jolt us into a new awareness of life. Grof's alternate paradigm strongly suggests there may be another way of looking at trauma that isn't pathology focused. His model speaks to having lost our purpose and our sense of connection, and not just with other people, but with the entire universe. This perspective has taught me that problems don't have to be conquered. Rather, as healers we are charged with relating to them differently, plunging into the mystery that isn't always explained by a diagnostic checklist. Suffering and sickness can better be seen as a void of sacredness. They carry messages from beyond about our own limited conscious awareness. They suggest there is a need for cleansing, to wash away parts that have become contaminated. But suffering and sickness can additionally remind us to sharpen talents that have been weakened due to neglect. Therapy is never as simple as curing with pills or with insights.

> *This is the first, wildest, and wisest thing I know, that the*
> *soul exists, and that it is built entirely out of attention.*
>
> —MARY OLIVER, POET

EIGHT

The Heroic Journey

All suffering prepares the soul for vision.

—MARTIN BUBER

The stories of trauma survivors and thrivers are frequently nothing short of heroic. These survivors are challenged by frightening circumstances. Wounded, hurt, confused, and cast into the throes of emotional seizures, they set out in search of survival but later want answers to the meaning and purpose behind it all. Much of that time they are lonely and isolated. Sometimes the suffering is a necessary catalyst, maybe even desirable at one level because it precipitates a subterranean exploration of the mind, something that in a serene life might never be done. Other times it is an extended despair-filled period that seems interminable, as if no end is in sight. But when clarity and healing finally blossom there is a simultaneous impulse to return to community and share the insights of what Joseph Campbell called the *hero's journey*. Severe trials and suffering can provide a glimpse of something profound, transcendent, and beyond narrow daily explanations of good and evil. These are the circumstances when awe is awakened. "The beginning of a mythic world or a mythic tradition is a seizure, something that pulls you out of yourself, beyond yourself, beyond all rational patterns" (Campbell 2004, 91). Eventually you walk through a door where life surpasses all previous understanding, where dualistic rules no longer apply, and people are no longer seen in pairs of opposites.

Campbell identified common steps (paraphrased here) that are part of a hero's journey. Each one has predictable challenges and gifts:

> *The Call to Adventure.* A chance encounter, perhaps a convulsing trauma, opens a window to a new but threatening and ominous world. We are pulled into a forest of

transcendent mystery and enter at the darkest emotional point where there is no path to be found.

Refusing to Heed the Call. Victims commonly deny what is happening. "Tell me it's not so" they cry out. Responding to fear, uncertainty, and the unknown, victims are initially reluctant to commit to major change. Resistance has set in. They balk at the thought of any transformative experience that could transport them into unfamiliar terrain, and resultantly fall back into old coping patterns.

Search for Supernatural Aid. They scream out, "I need God's help, or at least a damn good therapist!" There may be prayers for a magical escape from the pain. Advice and guidance start to come from seemingly strange sources that are described as angels, voices, serendipitous social contacts, the people who fortuitously show up. They rely on myths that don't have to be true, reasonable, or rational, but they are acceptable at the time.

Crossing the Threshold. Victims (or heroes-to-be) boldly step into uncharted territory, an emotional location where they have never sojourned before. Theologians call this place the *dark night of the soul.* Danger, despair, and hopelessness may be all that is felt.

The Trials. Things look bleak. Familiar and secure footholds can't be found. Challenges, obstacles, and tests abound. At first they seem insurmountable. Some invisible and benign power intercedes, perhaps *Spirit.* The victim rises to the occasion and courageously survives all the ordeals, conquers all the demons, and comes away from the trauma stronger and wiser, filled with wisdom and insights.

Refusal to Return. Having experienced what felt like a near-death experience and then having tasted sweet victory, surprisingly the conqueror of dragons (usually his or her inner demons) is reluctant to return home and share the resultant teachings. Yet, the feeling of being commissioned and obligated to do so as a member of a now larger community persists.

The Return, Rescue from Without. Mission accomplished and understanding the bigger dimensions of the experience, a return is made. Back again, new tests are encountered from outside oneself. External support is required and often it comes from someone awaiting a new kind of relationship with the hero.

Master of Both Worlds. Once a victim, now a heroic thriver, a new status is experienced. Much like the traditional makings of a shaman, this wise figure feels steeled and can now enter and exit troubled worlds and alternate realities at will with remarkable ease.

This is the hero's journey. It can be the victim's path too—the journey of psychotherapy when done spiritually. This is also the experience of thrivers. They move from a simple view of the world and are transported by crisis to a new level of meaning, acceptance, and understanding. A dichotomous or dualistic worldview no longer suffices. They have entered a realm of understanding that supersedes anything ever encountered before. There is a compelling desire to share the resultant intuitive flashes lest the doors of expanded consciousness unpredictably slam shut.

When SITEs respondents spoke of a spiritual awakening following a brush with death it was as if trauma had introduced them to a much bigger world, another reality, a more complex way of perceiving and being in the world. And it felt good, very good. They became softer on the outside but stronger on the inside. Paradoxically, something awful introduced them to something resplendent.

Thrivers are our modern mythmakers. Their stories make sense of a mysterious and frightening world and they fashion a path for others that follow. Thrivers face dragons; the first ones encountered are usually their abusers. The dragons that follow are mostly demons of their own making, internal conflicts. During the dark nights on the hero's journey, when there was no clear direction to be found, they cut a path of their own making. In the end they entered into a world of bliss, an unexpected destination, one that was made possible by their willingness to approach suffering in a unique way, by becoming intimate with it.

It was before trauma that many people wore illusory masks. The masks worn represented idealistic versions of who they wanted to be. But following trauma, a descent into hell, and a heroic return, masks no longer seem necessary. Even the word *heroic* feels a bit unnecessary because what the thrivers really came to grips with was their unity with everything and everyone in their world. Connected in this way it became difficult to hate, to stereotype people, and to be angry any longer. Their bliss was the quiet feeling of love that washed over them, an *agape* love that when expressed sought nothing in return. They would never be the same again, but not in the way the media would depict it, as damaged and depressed for life. Rather, these thrivers were uplifted to an entirely new way of experiencing and enjoying their existence on the planet.

When we talk to someone who suffered from a major illness and was written off for dead, only to begin a decline to the precipice of death and suddenly rebound, we call that a *near-death experience*. I'm not referring to a superstitious or confabulated event, but a real encounter with death. With it the person undergoes a collapse of ego; the baggage of socialized existence falls away and with it, astonishing relief is felt. Prior feelings of alienation are suddenly supplanted by an amazing sense of connectedness to the entire world, even the cosmos. The bliss, peace, and serenity that follow feel like the trauma was paved over with some kind of neutralizing agent. Something that once was horrific ends up becoming something transformative. Joseph Campbell (1991, 39) has summarized this string of events by writing, "The dark night of the soul comes just before revelation."

Emerging into a new world, old agendas fall aside. Envy and prejudice disappear. There is a deep sense of being present with life and a commitment to do what one must absolutely do to be one's most genuine self. That is what is meant by bliss, following an authentic life course. Now with life on track one becomes an unstoppable force. Again, in the words of Joseph Campbell (2004, xxiv), "Bliss is the welling up of the energy of transcendent wisdom within you." It was there all along, but an earthshaking event had to awaken the force and align it with its true developmental course.

So, trauma doesn't always destroy people. It often remakes them into bigger, better, stronger, and more humane individuals. Thrivers report how scorching personal tests often turn out to be life vivifying. Then for the therapist who travels alongside such amazing patients, we too are uplifted. As psychotherapist Bradford Keeney (1996, 91) wrote, "Nothing brings forth more bliss than helping others find their bliss. When we collaborate in the search for bliss, everyone is touched and fulfilled. There we find ourselves inside the hearts of one another, dancing in the light of one spiritual family."

Is this just New Age dreaming and "pie in the sky" wishful thinking? No! Sufficient research has been completed to convince trauma experts that amazingly positive outcomes routinely occur after searing pain. It is all in the relationships, how patients relate to the trauma and we relate to the patient. If we only study trauma or only study patients, we will not be touched in the same meaningful ways.

> *Whoever survives a test, whatever it may be,*
> *must tell the story. That is his duty.*

> —ELIE WIESEL

Resources

There are many texts that can help therapists expand the assessment process beyond psychological abnormalities. Let's review a few of the therapist-friendly books arranged by topic:

Biochemistry of Alcoholism: *Seven Weeks to Sobriety* (1997) by Stephanie Mathews-Larson offers a diagnostic screener to assess a patient's *alcohol biotype*. Once there is an understanding of the way in which the patient's unique body responds to alcohol, the book guides the reader through the development of a very specific treatment plan that goes well beyond character deficits, offering a comprehensive nutritional plan that augments more traditional methods of recovery.

Biochemistry of Anxiety: Henry Emmons offers old and new screening information and responsive remedies for anxiety in his book *The Chemistry of Calm* (2010). Nutritional aids and physical activities are described.

Biochemistry of Depression: *The Chemistry of Joy* (2005) by Henry Emmons, MD. Using Western science and ancient wisdom traditions, this book offers guidelines and questionnaires to understand a patient's unique mindbody. Solutions goes well beyond the usual prescription of pharmaceuticals and include holistic diet and exercise plans.

Neuropsychiatry: *Change Your Brain, Change Your Life* (1999) by Daniel Amen, MD. This book provides questions to be asked of patients, brain region by brain region, with explanations of what behavioral and cognitive issues and corresponding treatments (with many natural remedies) are available.

Neurotransmitters and Biochemical Factors: *The Edge Effect* (2005) by Eric Braverman, MD. This book includes screening questions that point to possible neurotransmitter deficiencies (acetylcholine, dopamine, norepinephrine, or GABA) that can give rise to anxiety, depression, insomnia, addictions, and memory problems. Suggested treatment approaches go well beyond traditional pharmaceuticals, and Braverman, a neuropsychiatrist, includes detailed dietary and supplementation plans.

Spiritual Assessment: *The Bliss Experiment* by Sean Meshorer (2012) provides easy to understand assessment and treatment guidelines including exercises for retelling stories, discovering meaning and purpose, releasing the past, forgiveness in child sexual abuse, anxiety, depression, and chronic pain.

References

Abidoff, M., et al. 2004. "Rhodiola rosea extract rhodax reduces inflammatory plasma C-reactive protein and creatine kinase in healthy volunteers. A placebo controlled, double-bind clinical trial." *Experimental Biology and Medicine.*

Amen, D. 1999. *Change your brain, change your life.* New York: Three Rivers Press.

Anthony, E. J., and B. J. Cohler. 1987. *The invulnerable child.* New York: Guilford.

Antonovsky, A. 1987. *Unraveling the mystery of health.* San Francisco: Josey-Bass.

Benson, H. 1976. *The relaxation response.* New York: Harper.

Blanchard, G. T. 2011. *The difficult connection.* Brandon, VT: Safer Society Press.

———. 2011. *Ancient ways.* Holyoke, MA: NEARI.

Bonnano, G. A., S. Galea, A. Bucciarelli, and D. Vlahov. 2006. "Psychological resilience after disaster: New York City in the aftermath of the September 11th terrorist attack." *Psychological Science* 17:181–86.

Borysenko, J., and G. Dveirin. 2007. *Your soul's compass.* Carlsbad, CA: Hay House.

Braverman, E. 2005. *The edge effect.* New York: Sterling.

Brelau, N., and R. C. Kessler. 2001. "The stressor criterion in DSM-IV posttraumatic stress disorder: An empirical investigation." *Biological Psychiatry* 50:699–704.

Brichenko, V. S., I. E. Kupriyanova, and T. F. Skorokhova. 1986. "The use of herbal adaptogens with tricyclic antidepressants in patients with psychogenic depression." *Modern Problems of Pharmacology and Search for New Medicines*, 58–60.

Broad, W. J. 2012. *The science of yoga.* New York: Simon & Schuster.

Brown, R. P., and P. L. Gerbarg. 2004. *The rhodiola revolution.* New York: Rodale/St. Martins Press.

Borysenko, J., and G. Dveirin. 2007. *Your soul's compass.* Carlsbad, CA: Hay House.

Campbell, J. 1991. *A Joseph Campbell companion.* New York: HarperCollins.

———. 2004. Pathways to bliss. Novato, CA: New World Library.

Carnes, P. 1997. *Sexual anorexia.* Center City, MN: Hazelden.

Cass, H., and K. Barnes. 2008. *Eight weeks to vibrant health.* Brevard, NC: Take Charge Books.

Cohen, D. 2002. *Turning suffering inside out.* Boston: Shambala.

Cohen, E. A., et al. 2010. "Rowers high: Behavioral synchrony is correlated with elevated thresholds." *Biology Letters* 6:106–108.

Cole, R. 1993. *The call of service.* New York: Houghton Mifflin Company.

Daedone, N. 2011. *Slow sex.* New York: Grand Central Publishing.

Demasio, A. 2005. *Descartes' error.* New York: Penguin.

Didato, S. V. 2003. *The big book of personality tests.* New York: Black Dog and Leventhal Publishers.

Dunn, J. 2012. "How to bounce back better." *Health*, September: 96–100.

Eisenberg, N. I. 2003. "Does rejection hurt? An FMRI study of social exclusion." *Science*, October 10: 290–92.

Elliot, D. M., and J. Briere. 1995. "Posttraumatic stress associated with delayed recall of sexual abuse: A general population study." *Journal of Traumatic Stress* 8:629–48.

Emerson, D., and E. Hopper. 2011. *Overcoming trauma through yoga.* Berkely, CA: North Atlantic Books.

Emmons, H. 2005. *The chemistry of joy.* New York: Fireside.

———. 2010. *The chemistry of calm.* New York: Touchstone Book/Simon & Schuster.

Farber, B. A. 1983. *Stress and burnout in the human service professions.* New York: Pergamon Press.

Feinauer, L. L. 1989. "Comparison of long-term effects of child abuse by type of abuse and by relationship of the offender to the victim." *American Journal of Family Therapy* 17:48–56.

Finkelhor, D. 1986. *A sourcebook on child sexual abuse.* Newbury Park, CA: Sage.

Fischer, L. 1983. *The essential Gandhi.* New York: Vintage Books.

Flach, F. 1988. *Resilience.* New York: Fawcett Columbine.

Frank, J. D., and J. B. Frank. 1961. *Persuasion and healing.* Baltimore: Johns Hopkins University Press.

Frazier, P., A. Conlon, and T. Glaser. 2001. "Positive and negative life changes following sexual assault." *Journal of Consulting and Clinical Psychology* 69:1048–55.

Freyd, J. J. 1996. *Betrayal trauma.* Cambridge, MA: Harvard University Press.

Gardner, D. 2009. *The science of fear.* New York: Plume.

Goldberg, C. 1986. *On being a psychotherapist.* New York: Gardner.

Goleman, T. 2001. *Emotional alchemy.* New York: Three Rivers Press.

Greenspan, M. 2003. *Healing through the dark emotions.* Boston: Shambala.

Grof, S., and C. Grof. 1989. *Spiritual emergency.* New York: Jeremy P. Tarcher/Putnam.

Guy, J. D. 1987. *The personal life of the psychotherapist.* New York: Wiley.

Haidt, J. 2006. *The happiness hypothesis.* New York: Basic Books.

Halifax, J. 1993. *The fruitful darkness.* San Francisco: HarperCollins.

Hanson, R. 2009. *Buddha's brain.* Oakland, CA: New Harbinger Publications.

Herman, J. 1992. *Trauma and recovery.* New York: Basic Books.

Horowitz, A. V., and J. C. Wakefield. 2012. *All we have to fear.* New York: Oxford University Press.

Hubble, M. A., B. L. Duncan, and S. D. Miller. 1999. *The heart and soul of counseling.* Washington, DC: American Psychological Association.

Janda, L. 1996. *The psychologist's book of self-tests.* New York: Perigree.

———. 2001. *The psychologist's book of personality tests.* New York: John Wiley & Sons.

Jones, B. 1995. *Listen to the drum.* Center City, MN: Hazelden.

Joseph, S. 2011. *What doesn't kill us.* New York: Basic Books.

Karr-Morse, R., and M. S. Wiley. 2012. *Scared sick.* New York: Basic Books.

Kessler, R. C., A. Sonnega, E. Bromet, M. Hughes, and C. Nelson. 1995. "Posttrauamtic stress disorder in the national comorbidity survey." *Archives of General Psychiatry* 52: 1048–60.

Kissel Wegela, K. 2009. *The courage to be present.* Boston: Shambala.

Kottler, J. A. 1991. *The compleat therapist.* San Francisco: Josey-Bass.

———. 1995. *Growing a therapist.* San Francisco: Josey-Bass.

Kottler, J. A., and J. Carlson. 2007. *Moved by the spirit.* Atascadero, CA: Impact Publishers.

Kottler, J. A., T. L. Sexton, and S. C. Whiston. 1994. *The heart of healing.* San Francisco: Josey-Bass.

Krasik, E. D., K. P. Petrova, G. A. Rogulina. 1970. "Adaptogenic and stimulative effect of golden root extract." *Proceedings of all Soviet Union congress of neuropathologists and psychiatrists.* May 26–29: 215–17.

Laing, A. 2006. *R. D. Laing, a life.* Gloucestershire, England: Sutton Publishing.

Lancaster, B. L., and J. T. Palframan. 2009. "Coping with major life events: The role of spirituality and self-transformation." *Mental Health, Religion, and Culture* 12:257–76.

Lazarus, R. S. 1984. *Stress appraisal and coping.* New York: Springer.

Lehman, D. R., C. G. Davis, A. Delongis, C. B. Wortman, S. Bluck, D. R. Mandel, and J. H. Ellard. 1993. "Positive and negative life changes following bereavement and their relations to adjustment." *Journal of Social and Clinical Psyhcology* 12:90–112.

Leopold, A. 1949. *Sand County almanac.* New York: Oxford University Press.

Lesser, E. 2005. *Broken open.* New York: Villard.

Levine, P. A., and M. Phillips. 2012. *Freedom from pain.* Boulder, CO: Sounds True.

Lewin, R. A. 1996. *Compassion.* Northvale, NJ: Jason Aronson.

Lilenfeld, S. O., and H. Arkowitz. 2012. "When coping fails." *Scientific American Mind,* May/June: 64–65.

Linely, P. A., and S. Joseph. Eds. 2004. *Positive psychology in practice.* Hoboken, NJ: Wiley.

Lopez, S. J., and C. R. Snyder. 2004. *Positive psychological assessment.* Washington DC: American Psychological Association.

Love, P. 2007. "Connections to a better self." In J. A. Kottler and J. Varlson, eds., *Moved by the spirit.* Atascadero, CA: Impact Publishers.

Mason-Boring, F. 2012. *Connecting to our ancestral past.* Berkeley, CA: North Atlantic Press.

Maté, G. 2010. *In the realm of hungry ghosts.* Berkeley, CA: North Atlantic Books.

Mathews-Larson, S. 1997. *Seven weeks to sobriety.* New York: Ballantine Books.

McTaggart, L. 2011. *The bond.* New York: Free Press.

McElroy, S. 2002. *Heart in the wild.* New York: Ballantine Books.

McGonigal, K. 2012. *The neuroscience of change.* Boulder, CO: Sounds True.

Mehl-Madrona, L. *Narrative medicine.* Rochester, VT: Bear & Company.

———. 2010. *Healing the mind through the power of story.* Rochester, VT: Bear & Company.

Meshorer, S. 2012. *The bliss experiment.* New York: Simon & Schuster/Atria Books.

Miphram, S. 2005. *Ruling your world.* New York: Morgan Road Books.

Moore, T. 2002. *The soul's religion.* New York: HarperCollins.

———. 2004. *Dark nights of the soul.* New York: Gotham Books/Penguin.

Moustakas, C. 1995. *Being-in, being-for, being-with.* Northvale, NJ: Jason Aronson.

Muller, W. 1993. *Legacy of the heart: The spiritual advantages of a painful childhood.* New York: Fireside.

Murphy, D., J. Durkin, and S. Joseph. 2010. "Growth in relationship: A post-medicalized vision for positive transformation." In N. Teharnit, ed., *Managing trauma in the workplace*. London: Routledge.

Murphy, G. M., and A. E. Moriarity. 1976. *Adolescent coping*. New York: Grune & Straton.

Ober, C. 2011. *Earthing*. Laguna Beach, CA: Basic Health.

Ogden, T. 1993. *Matrix of the mind*. Northvale, NJ: Jason Aronson.

Pearsall, P. 2003. *The Beethoven factor*. Charlottesville, VA: Hampton Roads Publishing.

———. 2007. *Awe*. Dearfield Beach, FL: Health Communications.

Perlman, H. G. 1979. *Relationship*. Chicago: University of Chicago.

Peterson, C., and M. Seligman. 2004. *Character strengths and virtues*. New York: Oxford University Press.

Pieper, M. H., and W. J. Pieper. 2003. *Addicted to unhappiness*. New York: McGraw-Hill.

Pinker, S. 2011. *The better angels of our nature*. New York: Viking.

Poulin, M. J., R. C. Silver, V. Gil-Rivas, E. A. Holman, and D. N. McIntosh. 2009. "Finding social benefits after a collective trauma: Perceiving societal changes and well-being following 9/11." *Journal of Traumatic Stress* 22:81–90.

Redl, D. 1969. *Children who hate*. New York: Free Press.

Saratikov, A. S., and E. A. Krasnov. 1987. "Clinical studies of rhodiola rosea." In *Rhodiola rosea is a valuable plant medicinal plant (golden root)*. Tomsk: Russia: Isdatelstvo Tomskogo University Press.

Satir, V., and M. Baldwin. 1983. *Satir step by step*. Palo Alto, CA: Science & Behavior.

Seligman, M. 2002. *Authentic happiness*. New York: Simon & Shuster.

———. 2011. *Flourish*. New York: Free Press.

Siebert, A. 1996. *The survivor personality*. New York: Perigree Book/Berkeley Publishing Group.

———. 2005. *The resiliency advantage*. San Francisco: Berrett-Koehler Publishers.

Siegel, D. J. 2010. *Mindsight*. New York: Bantam.

Skovholt, T. M. 2001. *The resilient practioner*. Needham Heights, MA: Allyn and Bacon.

Smith, A., S. Joseph, and R. D. Nair. 2011. "An interpretive phenomenological analysis of post-traumatic growth in adults bereaved by suicide." *Journal of Loss and Trauma*. Online first publication. http://www.informaworld.com/smpp/content~db=all~content=a936083790~frm=abslink.

Somé, M. 2004. *Of water and the spirit*. New York: Jeremy P. Tarcher, Putnam Books.

Somé, S. 2003. *Falling out of grace*. El Sobrante, CA: North Bay Books.

Spasov, A. A., 2000. "A double-blind, placebo-controlled pilot study of the stimulating and adaptogenic effect of rhodiola rosea shr-5 extract on the fatigue of students caused by stress during an examination period with a repeated low-dose regimen." *Phytomedicine* 2(7):85–89.

Strayer, D. L., and J. M. Watson. 2012. "Supertaskers and the multitasking brain." *Scientific American Mind*, March/April: 22–29.

Tarrant, J. 1998. *The light inside the dark*. New York: HarperCollins.

Taylor, S. 2012. "Transformation through suffering: A study of individuals who have experienced positive psychological transformation following periods of intense turmoil." *Journal of Humanistic Psychology* 52(1):30–52.

Tedeschi, R. G., and L. G. Calhoun. 1995. *Trauma and Transformation*. Thousand Oaks, CA: Sage.

Tedeschi, R. G., and R. J. McNally. 2011. "Can we facilitate posttraumatic growth in combat veterans?" *American Psychologist* 66:924.

Temple-Raston, D. 2005. *Justice on the grass*. New York: Free Press.

Tolle, E. 2004. *The power of now*. Novato, CA: New World Publishing.

Townsend, S. 2002. *The joy of burnout*. Shanklin, Isle of Wight: Skyros Books.

Van Dernoot Lipsky, L. 2009. *Trauma stewardship*. San Francisco: Berrett-Koehler Publishers.

Warschaw, T. A., and D. Barlow. 1995. *Resiliency*. New York: Master Media.

Welwood, J. 2002. *Toward a psychology of awakening*. Boston: Shambala.

Wickelgren, I. 2012. "Trying to forget." *Scientific American Mind*, January/February: 33–39.

Wolin, S. J., and S. Wolin. 1993. *The resilient self*. New York: Villard Books.

Yalom, I. 1980. *Existential psychotherapy*. New York: Basic Books.

Yates, P. M., D. Prescott, and T. Ward. 2010. *Applying the good lives and self-regulation models to sex offender treatment*. Brandon, VT: Safer Society Press.

Young-Eisendrath, P. 1996. *The gifts of suffering*. Reading, MA: Addison-Wesley Publishing.

———. 1997. *The resilient spirit*. Reading, MA: Addison-Wesley Publishing.

Zolli, A., and A. M. Healy. 2012. *Resilience*. New York: Free Press.

About the Author

GERAL BLANCHARD, LPC, has served both the victims and perpetrators of trauma for over 40 years. He is the author of *The Difficult Connection* and co-author of *Sexual Abuse in America*. Geral's long-standing interest in the many ways indigenous cultures inform today's psychology is showcased in his book *Ancient Ways: Indigenous Healing Innovations for the 21st Century*. After residing in Wyoming for decades, Geral now maintains a private psychotherapy practice in Des Moines, Iowa, and regularly travels to Africa, South America, and Canada to work with traditional healers. He can be reached at blanchardgeral@gmail.com.